"Why don't you leave me alone?" she asked

"Because you amuse me," Matt said, smiling. "The rage in your eyes makes you look almost as human as you did when I stopped kissing you in the elevator. I had a bet with myself about how long it would take to thaw you out."

Her body tense with impotent rage, Leigh asked coldly, "And did you win?"

"You know I did," he said softly, his gray eyes focused on her mouth making her self-conscious.

Leigh wanted so badly to hit him that her whole body shook with the desire. He grinned hazily at her. "Not in public, Leigh," he advised. "Your fiancé would be shocked and it would cause a scandal."

She thought desperately of some way to wipe the lazy smile off his handsome face. If only she could hit back at him....

Other titles by

CHARLOTTE LAMB
IN HARLEQUIN PRESENTS

CALL BACK YESTERDAY 253
DISTURBING STRANGER 268
AUTUMN CONQUEST 273
THE LONG SURRENDER 277
THE DEVIL'S ARMS 286
FORBIDDEN FIRE 298
DARK MASTER 305
TEMPTATION 310
DUEL OF DESIRE 314
POSSESSION 321

Other titles by

CHARLOTTE LAMB
IN HARLEQUIN ROMANCES

FOLLOW A STRANGER 1722
CARNIVAL COAST 1751
A FAMILY AFFAIR 1803
SWEET SANCTUARY 1938
FESTIVAL SUMMER 2083
FLORENTINE SPRING 2103
HAWK IN A BLUE SKY 2161
MASTER OF COMUS 2181
DESERT BARBARIAN 2206

Many of these titles, and other titles in the Harlequin
Romance series, are available at your local
bookseller. For a free catalogue listing all available
Harlequin Presents and Harlequin Romances, send
your name and address to:

HARLEQUIN READER SERVICE,
M.P.O. Box 707,
Niagara Falls, N.Y. 14302
Canadian address:
Stratford, Ontario, Canada N5A 6W2

CHARLOTTE LAMB

pagan encounter

Harlequin Books

TORONTO·LONDON·NEW YORK·AMSTERDAM
SYDNEY·HAMBURG·PARIS·STOCKHOLM

Harlequin Presents edition published December 1979
ISBN 0-373-70828-9

Original hardcover edition published in 1978
by Mills & Boon Limited

CHAPTER ONE

Leigh sipped her drink, listening politely for the third time to a lengthy description of how her Uncle George had found his way across country to the church. Portly, serious, he was beginning to get confused as he narrated the route, and across the room he was being observed with a watchful eye by his wife, who caught Leigh's glance and winked.

A moment later she joined them, smiling at Leigh, her small, thin face indulgent as she slid an arm through her husband's, saying, 'I really think it's time we thought about getting back to the children, George. It's getting late.'

Slightly owlish, he looked at her affectionately. 'Who's driving, Maureen?'

'I am,' she said firmly, and for a moment their eyes met in a little smile, before George put down his glass and said regretfully, 'Nice to have seen you again, Leigh. I hope we meet up again before you get married.'

She smiled back, and Maureen, kissing her, whispered, 'When is the wedding, darling? Send me a present list in good time, won't you?'

When they had gone, making warm goodbyes to the bride and groom, Leigh stood observing her family with a thoughtful eye. They were a widespread but united group, cheerful, noisy and thoroughly enjoying this chance to retail the gossip of the last months to each other. They met at weddings and christenings, and took

5

the opportunity to catch up with each other's lives. Sometimes a year would pass before they met again, and on these family occasions they chatted eagerly to each other of what had happened since the last time they met. There were the usual intimacies between various branches of the family, who met more often, and these tended to congregate in little clumps, eyeing the rest curiously. Children ran about the large room, shouting, their mothers vainly pursuing them. The voices rose in a swell of chatter, punctuated by laughter. Outside the summer sky was blue, and Leigh could see the white sway of pear blossom in the wind.

Just as she finished her drink she saw her cousin Ann at the far end of the room by the open door into the garden, and began to walk towards her, smiling. For several summers she and Ann had spent their holidays together as children at a small house in Cornwall which their parents had shared as a holiday home. The close relationship had continued off and on for the rest of their adolescence, but during the past year she had seen very little of Ann, who had got a job in London with the large newspaper organisation, World Gazette, which owned both a daily paper and several magazines.

Rather tall, with a pale-skinned oval face and wide, long-lashed blue eyes, Leigh had a natural elegance which gave her graceful, slender body a style and flair which made her catch the eye. Her long, sleek pale blonde hair was woven into a smooth chignon at the back of her head, emphasising the cool proportions of her features.

She was not unaware of the glances which followed her across the room, and smiled as she caught familiar faces among the crowd, stopping to speak to several relatives whom she recognised.

In the peacock blue suit she was wearing she stood out

among the floral hats and pastels of her relatives, and several appreciative male glances followed her.

'Ann!'

The small, dark girl she spoke to turned with a curious, haunted expression in her brown eyes and gave her a stiff-lipped smile.

'Hallo, Leigh.'

Leigh frowned. 'You don't look well. Is something wrong?' She studied her cousin's face closely, reading lines of strain in the soft cheeks and around the warm eyes.

Ann tried to smile again, but her lips trembled. 'Oh, I ...' Her voice died away and she turned and dived hurriedly out through the open door into the garden beyond. Anxiously Leigh followed her and found her standing under the pear tree, her dark head against the rough bark of the trunk. A few white petals floated down to rest on her hair like confetti.

'What is it?' Leigh asked gently, resting a comforting hand upon the other girl's thin shoulder.

'I'm fine,' Ann said huskily.

'You sound it,' said Leigh, smiling at the bent head. Looking around, she saw nowhere to sit, so with a grimace she sat down on the neatly mowed grass and patted the ground. 'Come on, sit down and tell me about it.'

Ann sighed and slowly sat down, leaning her back against the pear tree. 'I ... I've got the sack,' she whispered.

Leigh looked at her in surprise. 'But I thought you were very good at your job. You seemed so happy working there.'

Ann's face seemed to break into a crumpled heap. Her eyes filled with tears and a sob came from her throat. 'I was,' she whispered shakily.

Leigh put an arm around her. There were three years between them. During their childhood she had been the natural leader, dominating the younger child, and had become accustomed to protecting Ann. The attitude held firm today. The younger girl was still the same helpless, emotional, tender-hearted Ann she had known in childhood.

'What went wrong?' she asked now, patting the heaving shoulders gently.

'I made the mistake of taking him seriously,' Ann said in sudden bitterness. 'I had been warned, but I was silly enough not to listen.'

Leigh's smooth brow creased in a frown. 'Who is he?' she asked carefully, staring at the tearwet little face.

'Matt!' The way Ann said the name was pathetic. Leigh could sense it even gave her pleasure to hear it on her lips, although she was crying as she said it.

'Matt?'

Ann looked at her, her lips trembling. 'Mattieson Hume,' she said. 'My boss.'

Leigh's eyes widened in astonishment as she stared at her. She had heard of Mattieson Hume, the head of World Gazette, but Ann's age and inexperience had left her imagining that her cousin worked there in some very junior capacity in which she would never be likely to come in contact with the great man himself. She thought carefully about the implications of Ann's muttered words, her blue eyes cool.

'You'd better start from the beginning,' she said slowly. 'What were you doing at World Gazette?'

Ann made a little face. 'Working in the typing pool,' she admitted. 'Matt has a secretary, Miss Harrison ... she's fabulously good-looking. But she's getting married next month herself. When she's busy Matt borrows a girl from the pool to work for him. That's how I met him. He called me in to type out some notes for him one afternoon. I couldn't finish them before five-thirty, so I worked on for an hour.' Her brown eyes swam with tears. 'I wanted to please him.'

Leigh's mouth tightened. 'And did you?'

'He was very nice to me when he came into the office and found I'd finished them,' said Ann, brushing a hand over her eyes. 'His dinner date had been cancelled, so he asked me if I'd like to eat out with him.'

Leigh coolly watched the warm glow in the girl's face. 'And after that?'

Ann sighed. 'He hardly seemed to notice me for weeks, then one night I was working late again, and he took me out afterwards.' She gave Leigh a secretive, bright-eyed look. 'He kissed me in the car before we said goodnight Oh, Leigh, you can't imagine how I felt!'

Can't I, thought Leigh grimly, watching the soft face glowing at her.

Ann seemed to be lost in dreamy reverie, her eyes on the blue sky. Leigh observed her for a few moments, then asked quietly, 'And then?'

Ann began to flush. 'Oh ... several times we had a date. He used to ask me suddenly out of the blue.'

'And you always went?' Leigh murmured grimly.

'I was crazy about him,' Ann said protestingly, as though being accused of something.

And he knew it, Leigh thought, her pink mouth tight. Aloud, she asked, 'So when did this romance start to go wrong?'

Ann looked down, her lips trembling. 'He ... he'd spoken to me about taking it all seriously,' she whispered. 'He said he hoped I wasn't building our friendship up into something big.'

'Which you were,' Leigh interpreted.

'I told him I knew we were just friends,' Ann said

defiantly. 'It was just an occasional date, nothing more.'
Her brown eyes met Leigh's assessing look. 'I thought
that in time it would be different. He liked me, Leigh—I
could tell. He kissed me so nicely, and he bought me
flowers and chocolates. He said I was very pretty, and
his eyes said it too.'

Damn him, thought Leigh, watching the lines of
strain around the girl's eyes and mouth.

'When did it all blow up?' she asked gently.

Ann sighed. 'There was a lot of gossip in the typing
pool, you see.'

I bet there was, Leigh thought.

'Some of it must have got through to Matt. He overheard some girls talking, I think. Anyway, he told me we
must stop seeing each other. H-He said a pl-pleasant
friendship was being turned into a great r-romance.' Her
voice broke several times as she spoke.

'You mean he sacked you to stop the gossip?' Leigh's
voice was hard.

Ann gave a tremulous little laugh. 'Oh, no. He didn't
sack me then.' She gave Leigh a faintly anxious look. 'I
thought, you see, that he'd change his mind. I thought in
time we'd start seeing each other again.' Her mouth
quivered. 'But then Cathy Lord came along . . .'

There had to be a counter-attraction, of course,
thought Leigh cynically. 'Cathy Lord?' she asked Ann.
'Who's she?'

'Her father is one of the directors of World Gazette,'
Ann said hopelessly. 'She's pretty, sophisticated and very
well off. She drives a red Jag and wears fabulous clothes.'

'And Mattieson Hume started to date her,' Leigh murmured. He would, of course.

'Oh, Leigh!' Ann began to sob, her face buried in her
small pale hands. 'I was so miserable, I lost my head.'

'What did you do?' Leigh asked, frowning.

Ann whispered through her fingers, her voice muffled. 'I ... I went to see him after work one night. There ... there was a scene. I got upset and I shouted. Next day I was transferred to one of the magazines. I start there next Monday.' Her body shook. 'Just like that.'

'So he didn't actually sack you, but transferred you?' Leigh asked.

'Just because I love him,' Ann wailed. 'He made me fall in love with him and then he dropped me like a hot brick!'

Leigh sighed. 'Darling, look at it this way ... you're well out of it. The man's obviously a bastard. Chalk it up to experience and forget him.'

'I can't,' wailed Ann, her eyes full of desperation. 'You don't understand, Leigh. I love him!'

'Poor Ann,' said Leigh, her cool face full of sympathy. Ann had always been so vulnerable, eager and exposed to life, taking knocks hard, warmly responsive to offered affection. Her parents had three older children and Ann had been the one who was slightly left out of things, too young to join the others at first, and then later, when they had grown up and married, remaining the last child at home, a little spoilt by her parents for a while, but always the odd man out.

Leigh had taken her under her wing when they were young, and she felt a protective impulse towards her even now. The only daughter of parents who were busy, capable and level-headed, Leigh had grown up differently. Learning at an early age to be independent, she had a strong sense of self-preservation where emotion was concerned. She had gone through a wild attack of love at seventeen, taking it badly, as she had measles ten years before. Recovering in time, she had decided calmly to defend herself in future against such excesses. Emotion was destructive, she thought, looking at Ann's pathetic little face. Poor kid! She was suffering like some dumb animal, unable to fight back, still in a heady trance over the bastard, while he, no doubt, was congratulating himself on escaping from the situation without bother.

A tall young man in a dark suit and crisp white shirt, a white carnation in his buttonhole, came wandering down the garden towards them. Leigh discreetly waved him out of sight, shaking her head. He made a loving, indulgent face at her and walked back into the house. A smile lingered on her face before she turned back again to Ann.

'You'll get over it in time, you know,' she said comfortingly. 'I know it's hard to accept that now, but you will.'

'You don't understand,' said Ann, her glance suddenly pricking with hostility. 'Girls like you collect men in hordes. You've always been able to twist them around your little finger, Leigh, and none of them has ever hurt you, have they? How can you guess how I'm feeling?'

Leigh did not look offended. She had met the same attitude before among her friends. They looked no deeper than the cool, glossy surface of her appearance, and Leigh's innate sense of personal privacy made it impossible for her to tell anyone about the violent emotional shock she had received as an adolescent. On holiday with her parents she had met a sophisticated older man with a roving eye, been totally swept off her feet by him and lived in a fool's paradise for two weeks before she discovered that he had a wife tucked away in the background. The discovery had come in time to prevent her making a complete fool of herself, but only Leigh had known that it would only have been a matter of time before she gave way to the ceaseless battery of her lover's desire for her.

The mere memory of her own helpless, infatuated passion for the man could make her lips tighten furiously even now.

'Do you resent my looks, Ann?' she asked her cousin gently. 'We can't ask to be born with or without attraction, you know.'

'Resent you?' Ann made a little grimace. 'No, of course not. If I'm truthful, I envy you. If I were as beautiful and sophisticated as you are, Leigh, I'd make Matt suffer the way I'm suffering now. But I can't. I'm too ordinary.' She gave a childish gulp. 'He was only amusing himself with me, I realise that now. I suppose I'll get over it in time. I must have been crazy to think someone like him would look twice at someone like me.'

'Nonsense. You're a very pretty girl,' said Leigh, drying her eyes firmly with a clean handkerchief. 'When you haven't been crying, that is.' Her smile gently teased, and Ann gave a soft hiccup of laughter.

'He'll marry Cathy Lord, of course,' she went on, still obsessed by her favourite topic. 'Her family have pots of money, so it's very suitable. He was afraid I would spoil things if any gossip started. Cathy Lord isn't the sort of girl who would stand for it.' Ann looked bitterly at the blue sky. 'She's the sort of girl who's had everything all her life and expects to be given whatever she wants. If she thought Matt was flirting with another girl, she'd be furious, and break off with him. She was even jealous of Miss Harrison, and everyone knows Barbara Harrison is madly in love with her fiancé.'

Leigh gently brushed the white petals from Ann's dark head. She kissed her cheek. 'There are plenty of other fish in the sea. Forget him.'

They walked back into the wedding and the young man who had wandered into the garden earlier at once handed them glasses of bubbly champagne. His brown eyes rested on Leigh's face as he smiled at her.

Leigh glanced sideways at him, giving him a meaningful jerk of the head in Ann's direction as some other guests began to dance. His mouth dented wryly, but he turned to Ann and asked, 'The music is infectious, isn't it? Feel like dancing?'

Ann looked at Leigh, half rueful. Leigh smiled at her. The young man took Ann's glass away and slid off with her in his arms, Leigh's eyes following them in satisfaction. She watched as Philip talked, his brown eyes warm on the other girl's small pale face. Gradually the lines of strain left Ann's mouth and eyes. She began to smile slightly and her body lost that stiff rigidity. Philip could charm the birds from the trees when he cared to exert himself, thought Leigh. When the dance ended he returned alone, having bestowed Ann safely with another young male guest. Together Philip and Leigh watched as the girl revolved in his arms later. It would take time, Leigh thought wryly, but the heart would heal.

Driving home later she stretched beside Philip in his car, her mind on Ann, a dark fury in her eyes as she thought of the ruthless selfishness of the man who had hurt her.

Philip gave her a questioning look. 'You haven't heard a damned word I said. What's wrong?'

'Something Ann told me,' she said, telling him about Mattieson Hume, her tongue scathing.

'Taking a girl out for a few dinner dates hardly makes him a close relation to Bluebeard,' Philip observed with masculine tolerance.

'He must have known what effect he would have on an unsophisticated kid like Ann,' Leigh snapped back. 'I know the type. I've no doubt it fed his ego to watch how starry-eyed she got. If he wanted some fun, why pick on an innocent child like Ann? Poor kid! Her mistake was in letting him get under her skin in the first place.'

Philip's face grew faintly pale. 'You'd never do that, would you, Leigh? Let a man get under your skin.'

'Not if I could help it,' she said, her mouth firm.

He stared ahead at the road in silence. After a few moments he said, half to himself, 'Why the hell I put up with it I don't know.'

She was taken aback by the violence of his tone. 'What?'

'You, my cold-headed, offhand darling,' he said bitterly. 'Why the hell are you marrying me, Leigh?'

'You asked me to,' she said coolly. 'Did you want me to refuse?'

'God knows,' he said explosively.

She raised the perfect dark line of her eyebrows. 'Are you talking seriously, Phil? Or is this just a brief tantrum?'

He suddenly pulled the car off the road into a layby and turned to face her, his arm along the back of the seat. He was an attractive man, she thought, her eyes calmly tracing his features. She had approved of his looks from their first meeting, and, as she got to know him better, she had increasingly approved of the man behind them.

'Just listen to me for a moment, Leigh,' he said breathlessly. 'Are you seriously happy with the way things are between us?'

She frowned at the sober tone of his voice and his brown eyes watched her face, a look of eagerness burning in them.

'Are you trying to hint that you've changed your mind, Phil?' she asked him quietly. 'Do you want to end our engagement?'

There was growing pallor under his skin. 'If I said I wasn't sure, Leigh? What would you say?'

'That we have a serious problem,' she murmured quietly.

Philip groaned. 'Oh, God,' he said under his breath. He took her face between his hands and stared into her eyes. 'Leigh, kiss me,' he said huskily.

She bent forward and kissed him tenderly, sliding her arms around his neck, and he sat still under the kiss, his eyes closed. A husky sound came from his throat. His arms closed round her tightly and he pushed her back against the seat, his mouth hungry, parting her mouth in endless exploration. Leigh yielded, her slender body plastic in his arms, kissing him back, her hands gently stroking his hair.

When he drew back, his face very flushed, his eyes bright, she smiled at him. 'And does that make up your mind for you, Phil?' There was affectionate teasing in her voice.

'You know damned well I'm insane about you,' Phil said unevenly. 'What bothers me is you, Leigh ... you're very responsive when we make love, but there's always that restraint. You hold something back. I never feel sure of you.'

'If you're asking if I love you,' she said gently, 'I do, Phil, very much. I thought you knew that. I'm sorry if you don't find my response satisfactory.'

He groaned again. 'You have the damnedest way of putting things! Darling, when you're in my arms I get dizzy and the blood rushes to my head. What do you feel?'

She frowned, a look of faint unease crossing her calm face. 'I enjoy it too, Phil. What do you want me to say?'

'God knows,' he said bitterly. 'That you feel the same way about me, I suppose.'

'We're two different people,' she pointed out. 'Just because I don't swoon when you kiss me it doesn't mean I don't love you. I enjoy being with you, I enjoy it when you make love to me. I'm looking forward to our wedding day. Don't ask me to be something I'm not. I thought you fell in love with me, not with someone else. Are you asking me to be different now?'

Philip slid back to his own side of the car and started the engine. His face was sombre as he drove away from the kerb, and Leigh sighed.

'If you would prefer to postpone our marriage,' she said lightly, 'that's up to you.'

'No,' he said.

'Are you certain, Phil?' She watched the dark structure of his face as street lamps shed their light over it.

'I'm going to marry you and take my chances,' he said.

Leigh smiled. 'Don't sound so resigned! If the prospect makes you gloomy we can go on as we are for a while. There'd be no harm done. I'm not in a tearing hurry to get married.'

'I'm well aware of that,' he said flatly. 'The trouble is, Leigh, I am. I want you so badly I'm going out of my mind, but if you don't feel the same way life will be hell for me.'

A curious little smile lit her blue eyes. She laid her hand on his knee and he started, looking down at her long fingers.

'I want you, Phil,' she said softly.

His eyes swivelled to her face. 'Enough to come to London with me this weekend?'

She looked at him, her eyes narrowing. 'What?'

He grinned. 'Oh, don't look so damned offended. I only meant I'd like to have you along. I'm not suggesting we anticipate the wedding, darling, much as I'd like to do just that.'

She considered the idea. 'This is the Euro Conference, is it?'

He nodded. 'Most of it will be pretty dull stuff, but there's a dance on the Saturday night, and unless you want me to spend it with the redheaded girl from Accounts you might like to come along for that.'

Leigh's eyes danced. 'Redheaded girl from Accounts?

Is that the one who glares at me every time I visit your office?'

Philip grinned. 'At the risk of sounding like Mattieson Hume, I've taken her out to dinner a couple of times, and she gives me the green light every time she sets eyes on me.'

Leigh thought of the girl with amusement. 'She's no vulnerable kid like Ann,' she commented.

'Tough as cow hide,' Philip agreed. 'She's going to the conference with Jefferson, the head of Accounts. His wife is in the States for three months, visiting their son.'

Leigh's mouth tightened. 'Poor woman.' She gave him a cool look. 'If she's going with Jefferson she won't have time to flirt with you, then.'

'Jefferson's married, I'm not,' Philip said teasingly. 'I'm a better prospect. But if you don't care to defend your property, Leigh . . .'

He pulled up outside her home and she turned to look at him, her eyes narrowed. 'Why have you taken her out to dinner, Phil?'

'Ha, jealousy at last,' he said, slightly breathless, but smiling. 'Purely business, actually. Clients who liked female company.'

She raised a cool eyebrow. 'Oh?'

Philip began to smile. 'Darling,' he said, reaching for her. 'Oh, darling!'

She surrendered, her mouth coolly receptive under his, and his arms tightened around her possessively. He stroked her blonde hair back from her face, looking into her blue eyes.

'Will you come?'

'If you want me to,' she agreed.

'I booked two rooms six months ago,' he said. 'I would have taken my secretary if you'd refused, but at that time it did cross my mind we might even be married by now.'

She was surprised. 'We'd only just met.'

His brown eyes rested on her cool face. 'I know,' he said thickly.

Leigh was touched. 'You're so impulsive, Phil. You're like Ann, you jump into situations without thinking.'

'And you think too damned long before jumping,' he said drily. 'Especially into bed.'

She laughed. 'I prefer to be wise before the event rather than after.' She gave him an odd little glance. 'If marriage had entered your mind six months ago why did you wait four months before proposing?'

'Because it hadn't entered yours,' he said in that dry tone.

She considered his answer thoughtfully. It was true She had liked Phil on sight, but she had not taken him very seriously for some time. By the time he had proposed she had begun to realise she was growing very fond of him, but she had asked for time to think before she answered. A week later she had accepted. As she had told him, she enjoyed his company and liked it when he made love to her. Her character made it unlikely she would ever meet a man more suitable as a husband, and, during the weeks of their engagement she had grown to love him dearly.

A kind, warm, impulsive man of thirty, Philip worked for a large Leicester electronics firm. His good looks were subdued. His nature was reflected in his eyes and mouth. He smiled a great deal and laughed often. She found him fun, and respected him.

'How did you know I hadn't thought of marrying you?' she asked, without disputing his assertion.

He grimaced. 'My darling, it was obvious.'

'Am I very obvious to you, Phil?'

'On the contrary,' he said. 'I often wish I understood you better. But one thing I was sure of ... I was mad to get you into bed, and you were still holding me at arm's length.'

She gave him a cool smile. 'And now?'

His face darkened. 'I wish I could say the situation had changed, but I suspect not.'

'And you still want to marry me?'

'For my sanity's sake I've got to,' he said, half laughing at his own passion.

'Oh, well, if your sanity is at stake,' she said lightly. 'I would hate to see you go out of your mind, Phil.'

He looked at her with a wry smile. 'There's a time when the laughter has to stop, Leigh. I passed that long ago with you, but you still play lighthearted games with me.'

'I thought we both agreed marriage should be fun,' she commented with a lift of an eyebrow.

'Fun!' he groaned. 'Darling, I'm at the end of my tether, and you still haven't got a clue, have you?'

Leigh's pink mouth curved in amusement. 'Oh, I think I've got a very good idea what's wrong with you,' she said, looking at him through her lashes. 'I'd say an earlier marriage would be my diagnosis rather than a later one.'

Phil stiffened. He watched her intently. 'Why?' he asked huskily.

She leant forward and kissed him, her cool hands framing his face. 'You ask the silliest questions, Phil,' she said, and got out of the car.

CHAPTER TWO

LEIGH worked as a secretary in a large firm of solicitors whose offices were in the centre of Leicester. She enjoyed her job, which was demanding, and had risen rapidly there to become secretary to the head of the practice. On the Friday following he eyed her leather suitcase curiously as he paused to leave the office at the end of the day.

'Going away, Leigh?'

She looked round, covering her typewriter swiftly. 'Yes,' she said. 'To London.'

'Alone?'

Something in his tone made a faint flush come into her cheeks. 'With Philip,' she said, almost defiantly.

'I see,' he murmured. 'Enjoy yourself!' With a slight smile he walked out, and she made a face at the door, knowing perfectly well what he was thinking, and finding it irritating.

When Philip opened the car door for her he glanced at her face with a frown. 'Something wrong?'

'Just my boss making cracks,' she said shortly.

Philip's mouth twitched. 'About the weekend? What did your parents say?'

She looked at him coldly. 'Just what he said ... enjoy yourself.'

Philip laughed, his brown eyes dancing.

She leaned back in her seat as they headed south, her face shadowed. Ever since the day of the family wedding

21

she had been in a peculiar frame of mind. The placid routine of her life had seemed perfectly satisfactory to her until she listened to Ann's heartbreaking confidences and then was brought sharply face to face with Phil's dissatisfaction with their relationship. She had been aware from the beginning that Phil was more desperately in love with her than she was capable of being with him, but her affection for him had seemed enough until that night. Now she felt she was faced with a problem she was not sure how to solve.

They arrived at the hotel just before nine. Dinner was almost over, and the head waiter had a sour look on his face as he showed them to a table. She sat down, her blonde head high, a cool expression on her face as she accepted a menu. Phil glanced at her across the table, his brown eyes alert to her mood.

'You've been looking grim ever since we left Leicester. We're here to enjoy ourselves, remember.' His glance pleaded with her. 'Are you still cross about your boss making cracks? He was only being funny.'

She lifted her white lids, her face carved in cold hauteur. 'I prefer to forget it,' she said.

Phil sat back as if she had slapped him. They ordered their meal and leaned back in silence. Her cool blue glance wandered around the lamplit room. It halted briefly, meeting the stare of narrowed grey eyes behind a wreath of blue cigar smoke, then, with a scornful flick of long lashes, moved on.

Phil leaned forward suddenly, capturing her hand. She looked at him, meeting his smile. 'Darling, something extraordinary happened today. I was going to tell you on our way here, but you were in such an offhand mood that I thought it could wait until later.'

The waiter appeared at their side and Phil released her hand to lean back. They began to eat their first course.

She looked at Phil curiously. 'Well? What was this interesting event you want to tell me about?'

'I was asked to go out to Saudi Arabia for six months,' Phil grinned. 'The firm are supplying electrical equipment to some company out there and they need a man on the spot to watch it all being installed. They asked me.'

'Why you?' she asked, pausing with a frown.

'I'm the computer expert,' he pointed out.

She continued with her food. 'What did you say?' she asked him quietly.

He reached across to seize her hand again, lifting it to his mouth, his lips tender against her skin. 'I told them to take a running jump,' he said. 'I couldn't ask you to postpone our wedding until I got back.' His eyes darkened on her cool face. 'And I was afraid that while my back was turned someone else might come along and steal you away from me.'

'Can I have my hand back?' she asked plaintively. 'I need it to eat my dinner.'

He grimaced, releasing her. 'Aren't you flattered that I should turn down a chance to see a fascinating country just because of you?'

'I think it would be an excellent idea,' she said, continuing to eat.

Phil tensed, staring at her. 'Why?'

'You said the other night that you wanted to be sure of me before we married,' she pointed out. 'This is your chance. If when you come back you haven't changed your mind, we'll get married.'

The waiter appeared before Phil could answer and whipped their plates away. Phil sat seething while he served the second course, his dark figure moving around them, while Leigh gazed calmly at the other guests. She caught sight of the redheaded girl from Accounts, eating with bald, flushed Jefferson, on the other side of the room, and a smile of distaste crossed her calm face as she glanced away. Her blue eyes trailed indifferently over the tables and for the second time came in contact with grey eyes. This time her glance was held. She sensed the man deliberately willing her to look back at him, and, her face unconsciously cold, she did so, inspecting him at her leisure, her oval features without expression.

He was a good three inches taller than Philip, his thick black hair threaded with silver at the sides, his face bearing the hallmark of power, a coldly cruel intelligence in the steely grey eyes. Beneath his dinner jacket his shoulders were wide and powerful, but his body was leanly fit as he lounged at his ease, eyeing her in his turn as curiously as she did him. Indifferently her mind played with the problem of his age. Late thirties, she decided. Under his dark brows his eyes narrowed in open speculation, and she gave him a last icy look before turning back to Philip.

'Your little redheaded girl friend from Accounts is here,' she murmured.

Phil turned, his eye sliding over the room.

'In the corner,' she said.

Phil lifted a hand in a wave and Leigh, turning her head to see the enthusiastic beam he got in return, smiled slightly herself, her face wry. There was no question but that Philip had made a conquest there, she thought. He turned back, his glance diving into her eyes to seek her reaction, and the eager appraisal brought a tolerant, humorous smile to her mouth. He looked like a little boy who had brought his mother something to admire.

'You should have come alone,' she said in mockery. 'Think how ecstatic she would be now.'

Phil's mouth turned down at the corners. He looked down at his plate with distaste. 'I'm not very hungry,' he said.

'Don't be silly, Phil. Eat it.' She was in a difficult mood

tonight—she knew that. Somehow she had been feeling edgy ever since Phil had asked her if she was as madly in love as he was—she had resented the question, although she had parried it. The only time she had ever lost control of her emotions she had found herself in a wild, emotional muddle which could have proved disastrous. She had made up her mind then never to do so again, and she knew she had not altered her mind. She had never pretended to Phil to be as passionately in love as he was —he had admitted as much. She offered him herself as she was, not as he might like her to be, and she looked at him with unconscious irritation as she remembered his remarks.

'About Saudi Arabia,' she murmured.

'Yes?' He looked apprehensively at her.

'Don't you think it might be the best thing for both of us if you went? You said the other night that you weren't certain about me, and it seems lunacy to marry feeling like that.' Her eyes were serious. 'Phil, I can't be a different person. If you fell in love with me as I am, how can you ask me to be different now? I haven't changed an inch. If anyone has, you have.'

He looked miserably at her. 'I don't want you to change, Leigh. I just want ...' His voice broke off on a sigh.

'What do you want?' she asked.

'You,' he murmured passionately, leaning towards her, his hand searching for hers, his fingers trembling as they covered hers on the tablecloth. 'You as you ought to be, a woman so much in love she can lose her head.'

The words sent a shiver down her spine. She withdrew her hand, frowning. He stared at her face, watching her expressions, their irritation visible in her blue eyes.

'As I said, you want me to be something other than myself,' she said flatly.

He sighed deeply. 'Maybe I ought to go to Saudi Arabia. Maybe absence will make a difference.'

The waiter brought their coffee and they drank it in silence, avoiding each other's eyes. Leigh rose after a few moments and looked at him calmly.

'I want to go to my room to unpack. Shall we meet in the bar in half an hour? You could ask Jefferson and your redheaded friend to meet us.'

He nodded. 'Just as you like.'

The sombre expression on his face touched her. She bent and kissed him deliberately on the mouth, her soft lips brushing his, and whispered, 'You could always make me jealous by flirting with her, Phil.'

His eyes began to smile as she withdrew and she smiled back. She walked out of the dining-room, unconscious of the glances which followed the slender sway of her body, the smooth blonde hair and cold face. Crossing the foyer, she went towards the lifts and pressed the button of one.

Footsteps behind her made her half turn her head. Out of the corner of one eye she recognised the man from the dining-room. He was standing just behind her, one hand pushing back a thick wave of silver-streaked black hair from his hard face.

The lift arrived and she walked into it. He followed. Glancing at her, he asked with a lift of his dark brows. 'Which floor?'

'Third,' she said crisply.

He pressed the button and the lift doors closed. She stood with a cool face ignoring him. He leaned back against the lift wall, his eyes travelling up and down her body in an insolent appraisal which annoyed her.

The lift stopped and she walked out of it, evading the man's grey eyes. She was surprised when he followed her. Her room lay at the far end of the long corridor and she could feel his stare during every inch of the way. Jerking open her handbag, she found her key and opened the door. Before entering her room she turned her head, bristling, and found him at her elbow. Shock made her start.

His eyes continued to sweep over her lazily, and hot colour began to rise in her face.

Slowly he held out a small pearl ear stud. 'You dropped this,' he said, and his tone mocked her.

Leigh almost snatched it from his palm. 'Thank you,' she said, her tone blistering.

'In the dining-room,' he added softly, as she turned to enter her room.

She halted, her cheeks burning. Her eyes stared at him, angry irritation in them.

'Why didn't you give it to me before?' she asked furiously.

He smiled lazily. 'I was enjoying the anticipation,' he said in mockery. 'Not to mention the view.' His eyes ran over her again.

For a moment Leigh's hand itched to slap his face and the blue fury of her eyes spat at him. He observed it with curiosity, as though interested to see what she would do. After a pause during which she fought a battle with herself and won, she said icily, 'Goodnight.' Going into her room, she closed the door and stood there, feeling her heart beating fast against the white silk of her blouse. A sensation of pure rage was filling her.

She could not remember ever having been so angry in her life. Something about the man had made the hair on her nape bristle. She fought back to self-control, her hands tense. A tap on the door made her whole body coil with anger. She opened the door, suspecting she would find him outside, but Phil stood there, a pleading look on his face.

'Darling,' he said softly, his eyes imploring. 'Leigh . . .'

Her blue glance moved past his shoulder. The other man was a few feet away, his head turned to watch them. Leigh stiffened. 'Come in, Phil,' she said in a loving tone, and stood back to let him pass, her eyes held by the grey ones behind him.

A faint, sardonic smile came into the hard face. She glared and closed the door on it.

Phil caught her to his body, his face buried in her hair. 'Leigh, don't let's quarrel. I want this weekend to be special.'

She could hear his heart beating against her as he held her, and she let herself lean against him, sliding her hands to his shoulders. Phil's mouth sought hers and she surrendered to him, her head tilted back to take his kiss. When he drew back he was darkly flushed.

'Do we have to go down to the bar?' he asked unsteadily.

She looked at him through her lashes, a teasing smile on her face. 'Are you trying to make the redheaded girl jealous?'

'Damn her,' he said thickly. 'Leigh . . .'

She evaded his eager arms, her head shaking. 'I want to unpack. Phil, I'll see you in half an hour in the bar.'

Reluctantly, Phil went out, and she set to work to unpack her clothes. When the room was tidy again she changed her clothes, finding a dove-grey dress in the wardrobe which she looked at for a moment before taking down. After changing she looked at her reflection thoughtfully. The dress had a demurely sexy style; the bodice very close-fitting, the neckline plunging in a deep v, while the skirt clung tightly to her slender hips. Through the smoky grey chiffon of the sleeves her arms glowed with a pearly shimmer, the cuffs buttoning at the wrist.

She left her room, satisfied with her reflection, and walked to the lift, only to halt in angry surprise as a man strolled out of a shadowy alcove beside it and looked at her with mocking eyes.

Lifting her chin, Leigh pressed the button. The man lounged on the wall, observing her in every detail.

'No earrings,' he murmured.

She stared ahead, giving no sign she had heard.

'Leigh,' he murmured under his breath, watching her.

She could not help a flicker of surprise that he should know her name. He caught the faint expression and moved closer as the lift arrived. She walked into it, tense as the doors closed and she was alone with him in the small grey box which was very like the colour of his steely eyes.

She stood, her face averted, and flinched as a finger moved to slide down the chiffon of her sleeve.

'Will you please leave me alone?' she suddenly erupted, turning on him furiously.

She saw the mocking satisfaction in his eyes as he suddenly shoved his hand down on the button panel, his palm flat. The lift gave a sudden jerk and stopped, shuddering. Leigh looked in stupefaction at him, her body tense.

'What have you done?' Her tone was suddenly shaking with alarm.

'We used to have one of these lifts,' he said calmly. 'There's a fault in the electronics. Sometimes someone would lean against the panel and stop the lift. The wires get crossed somewhere and the lift refuses to move at all.'

She was speechless, her eyes staring at his calm face, with blue rage sparking from them.

He folded his arms and surveyed her casually. 'It should take the engineer about half an hour to put things right. But first they'll have to find the engineer.' He gave her a sardonic smile. 'I'm afraid your boy-friend will have to wait a long time in the bar.'

'I'll report you to the hotel management,' she said fiercely.

He laughed. 'Oh, come on, you can do better than that. What happened to the icy calm with which you brushed off the boy-friend when he got too amorous?'

Her cheeks burnt under his watchful stare. 'What are you talking about?'

'During dinner,' he murmured, 'each time he tried to touch you, he got the slow freeze of those big blue eyes. I could feel his desperation from where I was sitting.'

She drew herself up coldly, her brows level above her blue eyes. 'I have no intention of discussing my fiancé with a perfect stranger.'

'Fiancé?' The question came sharply.

Leigh held out her left hand. His grey eyes flashed over her ring and the hard mouth indented. 'Diamonds. A girl's best friend—nice ones, too. How long has it been on your finger?'

'Two months,' she said, her mouth biting out the words. His questions irritated her intensely, but he had a way of asking them which made it somehow hard to refuse to answer.

He slid his hands into his jacket pockets, leaning back, his eyes on her cool face. 'And he's been on his knees ever since he proposed, I suppose, which is where you intend to keep him ...'

She had a shock at the biting irony in the remark. Her eyes darkened with rage. She looked at him, feeling the most intense hatred she had ever felt for anyone in her life. Although she angrily rejected the suggestion, there was sufficient truth in what he had said to make her violently resentful.

'If I were in his place,' he said lazily.

'Which you never would be in a million years,' she flung, unable to resist the temptation of a retort.

Undeterred, he smiled. 'If I were him I'd kiss you until you couldn't get off your knees, Leigh.'

Hot colour flowed up her face and she was furious with herself for betraying any reaction to the insolent remark at all.

Their eyes clashed across the small space of the lift. A sudden sense of panic made her breathe in shallow rapidity, her breast rising and falling fast. She could not even phrase a bitter reply. She was too knocked off balance, both by what he had said, and the cold, hard look on his face.

He waited for a moment, then a mocking smile twitched at his mouth. 'Which is precisely what I'm going to do now,' he said very softly, watching her.

Unknowingly, her face reflected an acute, bitter tension. Her eyes stretched wide, her cool pink mouth began to tremble. She took a backward step, coming up against the steel wall of the lift. He advanced deliberately.

'If you touch me I'll scream the place down,' she whispered through dry lips.

He placed his hands on the wall behind her head, enclosing her. His smiling, lazy eyes ran over her white face. She stared back, unable to move, conscious of a chaotic turmoil rising in her body.

'You wouldn't dare,' she said jerkily.

He laughed at that. 'I always take a dare, especially from a mouth like yours,' he told her tauntingly.

'Don't touch me,' she ordered, trying to hold herself stiffly.

'I'm not your tame fiancé, Leigh,' he said sardonically. 'I give orders, I don't take them.' His body leaned forward until she could feel the inexorable weight of his hard thighs against her, and her pulses began to beat so fast she was dazed and incapable of thinking straight. Never in her life before had such a sensation swept over her.

Her blue eyes focussed helplessly on his face. At such close quarters the sheer sexual drive of the man was devastating. Trembling, she felt the impact it was making in her own body, and, driven by darker instincts than she had ever felt before, descended suddenly from icy wrath to a humiliated, whispered plea for mercy. 'No, please . . .' Her voice was shaking as her eyes watched the long, hard, implacable mouth move down to take possession. Every nerve in her body was crying out in panic.

She tried to struggle, twisting between his hands. Against her mouth he murmured coldly, 'Keep still or you'll make me angry.'

Leigh's brain told her to ignore the softly spoken threat. She only had to scream, to fight him, she thought, for him to leave her alone. But instincts older than time dictated that she obey him. The threat of disturbing masculine violence had affected her at a primitive level which her brain could not reach. Until this moment she had felt she was in control of her life, priding herself on her ability to shape her world to suit herself. When Phil kissed her, however passionately, his caresses pleaded, as if it were she who controlled what happened between them.

For the first time in her life she found herself helpless in the grip of another human being's iron will power, and the experience was shattering. His hands tilted her head back, leaving her totally at his mercy, the savage, bruising pressure of his mouth forcing her submission, grinding her lips apart. He made no concessions. There was no question as to who held the whip hand. Her proud dignity fell away from her and dark colour began to burn in her face and throat as new feelings began to surge through her.

When he removed his lips and began to slide them silkily down the side of her throat, his fingers caressing the nape of her neck, she stood, shivering, breathing so erratically that it hurt her lungs. He raised his head and looked at her through half-lowered lids, acutely observing her flushed rigidity. Lowering his hands, he took her wrists and placed her arms around his neck, still watching her. She quivered but made no protest. His hands lay flat on her midriff while he stared into her wide, dazed blue eyes. She felt them glide upward until they covered her breasts. A long hoarse cry came from her and her lids closed helplessly.

His hard mouth was on her own in the next second. Leigh's heart was racing. She felt boneless, as though hardly able to stand. She arched towards him as though he were a magnet drawing her inexorably, and his hands gripped her back, pulling her closer until their bodies clung. Her lips parted, responded, burning for deeper contact. Quite unconsciously her hands were moving over his hair and neck in little, restless movements.

She barely understood when his fingers gently pulled down the zip of her dress, the powerful hands stroking over her naked shoulders and down her back. He pulled out the pins and her blonde hair tumbled down around her face, but the slender body in his arms made no sign of protest, pliant under the caress of his strong mouth and hands, totally responsive to his stark masculinity.

When he stopped kissing her she was shaking, her lids closed over the blue eyes, her parted mouth swollen with the long exchange of passion. For a moment he looked into her face intently. She opened her eyes to look back at him helplessly.

Abruptly he released her and she swayed backward, her legs shaking under her, her dress falling off her shoulders, revealing the white gleam of her skin, her blonde hair tumbled loosely around her face. The cool façade had cracked wide open. She almost fell as the support of his body was removed. For a moment she was totally off balance, emotionally and physically.

The grey eyes watched, alight with sardonic mockery, and she stared back at him, her eyes dazed.

'Perhaps I should give your fiancé a few lessons,' he murmured drily.

She heard voices at a distance. 'The engineer,' he said with a twist of his hard mouth. 'In the nick of time!'

Leigh hurriedly began to pull herself together. Her hands shook as she pulled up her zip, began to pin back her hair, bitterly aware that all the time he lounged easily against the wall, watching.

'Your lipstick needs some running repairs, too,' he told her mockingly.

She got out a handkerchief and bitterly wiped her mouth as if removing all traces of his kisses. He laughed under his breath.

'Beautifully done, but too late, Leigh,' he said softly.

She looked at him with intense hatred. 'You're the most loathsome man I've ever met in my life,' she said between her pale lips. Her trembling hands renewed her make-up and inspected her hair. By the time she had restored the elegant exterior of her appearance, she felt the lift give a sudden jerk and begin to move downward.

He did not move, his eyes intent on her profile. She felt his gaze as though it burned her very skin.

Softly, he murmured, 'Another minute in my arms and you would have been unable to stand on those delectable legs, Leigh. I'm sorry for your fiancé. He doesn't know what he's missing. You can be quite a woman.'

She ignored him. The lift doors slid apart and she stepped out into the foyer. Phil, his face alarmed, was waiting there. He caught her into his arms, kissing her cheek. 'Darling, I was so worried ... were you frightened?'

Deeply conscious of the man walking out behind her, she deliberately turned her head to meet Phil's mouth. 'I was terrified,' she said, in absolute truthfulness. 'It was horrible!'

Phil led her into the long cocktail bar and helped her, as though she were an invalid, to sink into one of the black leather couches. The redheaded girl gave her a quick, hostile look. Jefferson, his bald head shining with perspiration, eyed her admiringly.

'What happened?' he asked. 'Lift got stuck?'

'An electrical fault,' she lied. Phil eagerly brought her a drink and she swallowed it far more rapidly than she would normally have done. She desperately needed the sting of the alcohol at that moment. Her knees were still shaking and her body felt unfamiliar, as if her cells had evaporated under the heat of the moments she had spent in the man's arms, leaving her in a state of helpless weakness.

As she lowered the glass to the table, her trembling fingers still holding it, she became aware of his presence beside their table. Her wide, stricken eyes flashed to his face. A sardonic smile flickered over his mouth.

'Well, well, my companion in captivity,' he murmured. He glanced around the table. 'Good evening. A most unexpected accident, wasn't it? How lucky that the engineer was on hand to deal with it.'

'Thank God he was,' Phil agreed. He smiled in his friendly fashion at the other man. 'Will you join us? What will you have?'

The grey steely eyes flickered briefly across Leigh's pale face.

'A whisky,' he murmured. 'Thank you.'

Phil beckoned the barman and gave the order. 'Soda?' he asked.

The grey eyes remained fixed on Leigh, who avoided his glance. 'Please,' he said softly. 'You're very pale,' he told her. 'Are you feeling better now?'

'Yes, thank you,' she said stiffly.

He looked at Phil. 'I'm afraid your fiancée was very disturbed by the incident in the lift. Her legs almost gave way under her.'

Leigh gave him a look of silent hatred. He smiled at her, his eyes taunting.

'In fact,' he added softly, 'she nearly fainted on me.'

Leigh could have screamed to relieve the bitter, burning rage which was consuming her. 'May I have another drink, Phil?' she asked huskily.

'Of course,' said Phil, but his eyes were anxious as they studied her face. 'You do look white, darling. Are you sure you're all right?'

'I'm perfectly fine,' she snapped.

The soft, mocking voice said, 'Nervous tension. I should leave her alone for a while. She'll feel better when she's had another drink.'

His whisky arrived and he leaned back, sipping it. Suddenly Leigh felt the hard pressure of his leg against hers and hurriedly withdrew her feet, curling them up under the seat out of his reach.

Her gin came, and she drank it, feeling incredibly thirsty, as though her mouth were dry with ashes.

'My God, you certainly needed that,' he said.

She could have thrown it in his face. Instead, she looked at the redheaded girl with a smile. 'I'm afraid I've forgotten your name.'

'Fiona,' said Jefferson, his eyes admiring the girl's slim body in the bright green dress she wore. She was a shapely creature in the thick woollen dress, her breasts high under the material, her waist tiny. She gave Leigh a polite pretence of a smile in return.

'You work for solicitors, don't you?' she asked Leigh.

'Yes,' said Leigh.

'Ah, a secretary?' asked the grey-eyed man.

Phil laughed. 'She's very good.'

'I believe you,' came the smooth reply.

Leigh looked at him with hatred. 'What do you do, Mr——?' She paused, indicating she did not know his name.

'Hume,' he said softly. 'Mattieson Hume.'

Leigh's face reflected her astonishment. Phil and she exchanged long looks, then Phil pursed his lips in a silent whistle.

Mattieson Hume's hard face moved enquiringly from one to the other of them. He had noticed the way they looked at each other.

'What do you do, Mr Hume?' Fiona asked, her green eyes smothered beneath a layer of thick make-up, her lids as bright as her dress.

'I work in the newspaper business,' he said, briefly smiling at her.

'Ooh, a journalist,' she said, impressed.

His mouth was wry. 'You could call me that.'

'Not a very apt description, however,' said Leigh, her eyes on her glass.

'How would you describe me, Leigh?' he asked, and there was laughter in his voice.

She lifted her eyes to survey him smoulderingly. 'Don't tempt me,' she snapped, before she had had a chance to consider the retort.

Phil's face held astonishment and apprehension. He put a hand over her knee warningly. She looked at him sideways and read the look in his face. She realised that he was thinking of Ann, imagining that her remark had had its roots in her view of Mattieson Hume's behaviour towards her cousin. Having spent that half-hour in the lift with the man she no longer doubted her cousin's story. For a short while she had considered the possibility that Ann's emotions had had little fuel provided by Mattieson Hume's own actions, but a man who could act as he had towards her in the lift could have deliberately made love to poor little Ann in the hope of seducing her, only to change his mind when she grew too fond of him.

Fiona was considering Phil out of her green eyes. 'I've heard a rumour that you may be going to Saudi Arabia for six months soon,' she said disconsolately.

'I was offered the chance,' he agreed. He glanced at Leigh. 'I turned it down, though.'

'Wouldn't Leigh let you take it?' Mattieson Hume asked him.

Phil flushed, taking the irony of the tone. 'I didn't want to go,' he said irritably.

'It would be fascinating,' Jefferson sighed. 'I'd give my eye teeth to have the chance of spending six months abroad being paid all that money.'

Leigh looked at Phil curiously. 'All that money?' she asked him.

'They offered me double salary to go,' he admitted.

Her eyes widened. 'Really?'

'You could save a fortune while you were out there,' Jefferson muttered. 'I would have thought you two would be glad of the extra money. Marriage is damned expensive, you know. I suppose you're looking for a house?'

'Not yet,' said Phil.

'When is the wedding date?' asked Mattieson Hume, leaning back, his head lying on the black leather couch, his hands in his jacket pockets. He had a lazy, casual way of doing everything which forced Leigh to notice him. Beneath that easy air was an enormous dynamism, as if the silken cloak of his manner hid a terrible power.

'We haven't decided on it yet,' she said firmly, meeting his grey stare with all the coldness she could muster.

Fiona was bored with this discussion of the wedding.

She looked across at Phil, her face restless. 'There's a band playing in the next room. Why don't we go and dance for a while?'

'Good idea,' said Phil, looking eagerly at Leigh.

'I think I'll go to bed,' she said. 'It's getting late. But you go, Phil.'

'Nonsense,' Mattieson Hume put in, before Phil could say anything in reply. 'Of course you'll dance.'

He was on his feet as he spoke, his hard hand lifting her as if she were a doll. Leigh wanted to scream or bite him, but she was helpless under his ironic gaze in public. She allowed him to push her inexorably towards the door. Phil, Fiona and Jefferson followed them. Leigh stared ahead, saying under her breath, 'Will you get your damned hands off me?'

'You say that so convincingly, Leigh,' he mocked. 'What a pity you lie in your teeth.'

She looked at him involuntarily.

His steely eyes danced, mocking her. 'You made it transparently plain in the lift that you liked having my hands on you,' he said softly.

They walked into the other room. It was a long, elegant place with silk brocade couches lining the walls, tables at which couples sat talking by the light of pink lamps, and a polished parquet floor on which a number of couples were moving to the music of a small band.

Mattieson Hume's arm suddenly slid around her waist and she gave a low murmur of surprised alarm. He looked down at her, pulling her closer. 'We came in here to dance, remember?'

'Not with you,' she said unsteadily.

'With me, Leigh,' he said, moving her into the throng of couples with a long twist of his lean body. Over his shoulder she caught sight of Phil's angry face. He was watching them intently.

Mattieson Hume swung her around so that she no

longer saw Phil. 'Your fiancé looks as if he's going to explode any minute,' he murmured, his dark head lowering to smooth her cheek.

Her pulses beat violently. 'You swine,' she said shakily. 'I detest you!'

She felt his lips quiver in a smile against her skin. 'You little liar,' he said in her ear.

'Why don't you leave me alone?' she asked in angry desperation.

'Because you amuse me,' he said, and his head pulled back so that he could smile into her bitter blue eyes. 'I enjoy seeing that frustrated rage in your eyes. It makes you look almost as human as you did when I stopped kissing you in the lift.' The grey eyes ran over her angry face. 'When I saw you in the dining-room you looked like the empress of ice and snow, haughtily untouchable, so I had a bet with myself about how long it would take to thaw a woman out of the block of ice you live inside.'

Breathing stiffly, her body tense with impotent rage, she asked him coldly, 'And did you win?'

The grey eyes focussed on her mouth, making her dance stiffly in his arms, deeply conscious of their glance. 'You know I did,' he said softly.

Leigh wanted so badly to hit him that her whole body shook with the desire. He grinned lazily at her, watching her expression.

'Not in public, Leigh,' he advised in mock gravity. 'Your fiancé would be shocked and it would cause a scandal.'

She lowered her blue eyes, her dark lashes sweeping down over her cheeks. She was aware of such hatred that she thought desperately of some way of wiping the lazy smile off his handsome face. If only, she thought, I could hit back at him ... and remembered with a shock hearing Ann say a very similar thing. Ann had groaned,

'If only I could make him suffer as he made me suffer!'

Leigh could imagine that many other women had said the same thing about this man.

She looked up suddenly to find him watching her, the smile absent from his hard face for a few seconds, and a curiously intent look in his grey eyes. There was an odd silence as their eyes met. Leigh felt her mouth go dry. His hand pulled her closer, and she sensed that the movement was involuntary. His cheek descended against hers and she began to tremble, as she had in the lift, shattered by the awareness of him that she felt.

For a few moments they danced in silence. Their steps flowed in harmony, their bodies seemed to cling without volition. She could hear his heart beating against her own and the warmth of his breath on her bare shoulders.

Then the music stopped and they halted near the edge of the floor, slowly drawing apart. Without looking at him she walked back towards where Jefferson was sitting, his disconsolate eyes on Phil and Fiona as they walked back together, talking.

'Well, thank you for the dance,' Mattieson Hume said. He glanced at Phil as he joined them, his eyes jealous. 'Goodnight. I think I'll have an early night.'

Leigh was sitting down, her head averted. She felt his light glance at her. Then he was gone and she almost collapsed with the relief of having his presence withdrawn. In his company she felt as if she were permanently on edge, as if any second something disastrous would happen. He was the most infuriating, detestable man she had ever met, and she yearned for a chance to revenge herself on him for his behaviour today.

Jefferson whirled Fiona away triumphantly, and Phil sat down and stared at Leigh's bent blonde head, his gaze brooding.

'What were you saying to Hume?' he asked her tightly.

She looked up, her face calm. 'As little as possible,' she said truthfully.

'You were dancing with him as if you were in a dream,' Phil added, the ragged tone of his jealousy apparent.

'I was thinking how much I would like to hit him,' Leigh said, still telling the truth. 'I've never met a man I hate as much as Mattieson Hume. I'd like to see him thrown into a river full of crocodiles!'

'Odd our meeting him here after what Ann told you,' Phil commented, his attitude relaxing a little. 'Mind you, I expect there was a lot of smoke and no fire behind her story. Ann seemed a rather over-emotional kid to me.'

'I believe every word of it,' Leigh said bitterly. 'Mattieson Hume is a first-class bastard and someone ought to flay him alive.'

Phil laughed. 'My God, you've got it in for him, darling! He's a good-looking brute, you must admit.'

'Brute is the operative word,' she snapped. 'I hope to God we don't set eyes on him again during the weekend.'

CHAPTER THREE

Next morning after breakfast Phil and his firm went off to the first session of the Euro Conference in the Conference Centre, leaving Leigh free for the whole morning to wander around the London shops and window-shop alone. She came out of the lift, her mind preoccupied with the problem of finding a present to take back for her parents. They collected Wedgwood china, and she wanted to find them a nice piece which would fill a hole in their collection, but was torn between a piece of jasper or a very delicate floral design which her mother preferred. Walking out of the hotel, her eyes abstracted, she did not notice the car which was parked at the kerb outside until a hand descended on her elbow, making her start, and she looked round into Mattieson Hume's face.

She stiffened. 'What do you want?' Her tone was freezing, but he appeared unconcerned.

'Get in,' he said, opening the passenger seat of the long ice-blue limousine.

She pulled back angrily. 'No, thank you,' she said in tones of biting displeasure.

His eyes mocked her. 'Want me to pick you up and throw you in?'

For a full moment they stared at each other, conflict raging between them. Leigh was unaccustomed to losing arguments. For years she had protected herself inside a shield of icy calm. Now she found her armour ineffective against the stark insistence of that hard male face.

She was conscious that when he said something he meant it, and that he would not hesitate for an instant in carrying out his threat. While she was meeting the ironic stare of his grey eyes, she was assessing her chances of getting away from him, and realising that they were nil. He moved faster, thought quicker and was more deadly than she was—a damned male scorpion, she thought bitterly.

His hand impatiently pushed her inside the car and slammed the door. She turned to jump out, but he was already round to his own side and sliding behind the wheel. She twisted the handle as he started the engine, but the door didn't move.

'It locks automatically on the dashboard,' he murmured drily, moving away into the traffic.

'You bastard,' she said under her breath, in a childishly raging tone.

He laughed, giving her an amused glance. 'The icy calm is peeling off again, Leigh. You'd better watch it. Where's the haughty dignity with which you punish your poor worm of a fiancé?'

'I do nothing of the kind,' she snapped.

'I've seen you do it,' he said calmly. 'One icy look from those blue eyes and he grovels. In his place . . .'

'I've heard all that before,' she said stormily.

He leaned back and one long hand slid silkily over her knee. 'So you have,' he murmured.

She slapped at his hand, but it had gone before she made contact, and instead she hit herself. He made a derisive sound.

'Where do you think you're taking me?' she asked him, somehow controlling her voice, the icy reserve in it uppermost although she could sense that he knew very well that beneath that lay the panic and fear of him which those moments in the lift had produced.

'I thought Hyde Park would be pleasant,' he said casually.

'Hyde Park!' For a second or two she was taken aback.

'It's a nice morning for a walk in the park, don't you think?' He sounded as though they were polite acquaintances, his eyes fixed on the thick traffic through which they were moving.

Leigh took a long, deep breath. 'Will you stop at the next corner and let me out, please, Mr Hume? Or do I have to shout for help to the next policeman I see?'

His head turned. The grey eyes were filled with laughter. 'If you look out of the car you'll see one right now,' he said mockingly.

She involuntarily turned her head. A young constable was strolling along the pavement, eyeing the shoppers without interest. Leigh's face betrayed her angry feelings of helpless impotence. She had not got the courage to make a scene in public, and he knew it. He was trading on it.

She looked back at him, flame in her blue eyes. 'You're quite detestable!' she snapped.

He laughed openly. 'You disappoint me. I thought for a moment you were going to do it.'

'What would you have done if I had?' she asked, suddenly curious.

He glanced at her through his lashes. 'Try it and see.'

His arrogant, careless tone infuriated her. A defiant look came into her eyes, a glint of angry determination which did not escape his shrewd appraisal. His smile broadened, then he swung the car left towards the inviting green shade of Hyde Park. Around the park the traffic swirled thickly, but beneath the trees the peace and brightness of the morning held a promise of refreshment.

The car slowed, drew into a car park and deftly slid into a vacant space. Tensely Leigh waited for him to unlock her door. He turned, his eyes very bright, and opened his own door. She fumbled quickly for the handle and found herself free. Scrambling out, she began to walk quickly away through the trees. It was not far to Marble Arch, she reminded herself. She would walk there and do her window-shopping.

He caught her up before she had gone far, his fingers catching her wrist and halting her.

'Let me go!' she demanded, facing him with a flushed face. 'I really mean it this time ... let me go or I'll scream until every policeman in ten miles can hear me!'

'No need to make that much noise,' he said with a grin. 'There's one over there.'

She glanced over her shoulder and saw the blue uniform advancing stolidly along the path not a few feet away from them. For a few seconds her innate dislike of a scene held her silent. Mattieson Hume watched her closely, a smile on his hard mouth.

His hand slid suddenly from her wrist to her waist and the small movement made up her mind for her. She pulled away violently and called, 'Officer!'

The policeman did not hurry his pace. Politely he came forward at the regulation pace and surveyed her. 'Can I help you, miss?'

'Tell him to leave me alone,' Leigh burst out raggedly, afraid she would lose her nerve if she didn't speak at once. 'H-he's bothering me!'

The calm official eyes moved to Mattieson Hume's face. Leigh, trembling a little, very pink, did not dare to let her own glance meet the steel of the insolent grey eyes. Instead she held her hands laced at her waist, looking appealingly at the policeman.

'I'm sorry, constable,' said that detestable voice, quivering with maddening amusement. 'Bridal nerves, I'm afraid.' He reached out and picked up her left hand before she understood what he meant to do, and flashed the diamond ring before the policeman's eyes. 'Just because I prefer a double bed while she prefers twin beds she's been treating me like a leper for the last half hour.'

'Oh!' exclaimed Leigh on a positive hiss of rage. 'Oh, you liar ... you ... Officer, don't take any notice of him. It isn't true!'

'My mother says a marriage depends on double beds,' Mattieson Hume said seriously. 'It keeps a couple together.' He slid a long hand around her neck, his fingers caressing her nape. 'After we're married, Leigh, I insist on a double bed.'

'I wouldn't marry you if you went down on your knees to me!' she said in shaky fury.

'Darling, how can you say that after the way you responded last night?' he reproached her.

She spun towards him, her face flaming. 'You know very well, you devil, that I had no choice!'

'I'm only human, Leigh,' he sighed, his face a mask of mock penitence. 'And we are getting married. Don't embarrass the officer with the details of our love life, darling.'

'Oh!' she half sobbed, glaring at him.

The policeman coughed, shifting his feet.

Mattieson put an arm around Leigh before she could get away, pushing her face into his shirt front, although she struggled every inch of the way. 'You must excuse her, officer,' he said. His hand held her head buried against him although she tugged to get free. 'She's very highly strung at the moment.'

'I understand, sir,' the policeman said. 'Good luck for the wedding. Personally, I couldn't agree more about the double bed. It's cheaper than a hot water bottle.'

Mattieson's laughter almost drove her mad. She began to struggle violently, but felt herself lifted into his arms, as easily as if she were a child, and carried, her face twisting to extricate itself from his shirt. He sat down with her across his lap and at last she was free, only to find herself sitting on the grass beneath the trees, the blue uniform already receding into the distance, and Mattieson Hume looking down into her face with a twist of mockery on his lips.

She looked at him, her eyes burning. 'I hate you,' she said, through lips which shook.

'Do you, Leigh?' He laughed, bending his head.

Leigh's heart beat with a mixture of rage and desire which deafened her. They kissed like enemies exchanging blows in a bitter battle, a wild, savage exchange which made her breathless. On the heels of rage came a stronger emotion, engulfing her before she had time to understand what was happening to her. Her traitorous body weakened, succumbing to the need to submit to him, and she drowned in sensuous sweetness, her hands moving over him restlessly, her head thrown back to receive his kiss.

When he pulled back his head they were both breathing fast, and she was almost dizzy, her arms locked around his neck, clinging to him, as if she were afraid of falling.

'You show hatred very excitingly, Leigh,' he murmured, his mouth sardonic.

Hot with shame and self-contempt, she struggled to get away, but he held her too tightly, his hands controlling her. She jerked backward and fell, rolling on to her back. Instantly he was beside her, his face staring down into hers as he held her immobile with one hand.

'At least you won't ever try to involve someone else in our little war, again, will you, Leigh?' he mocked. 'You're a clear-headed girl. Face facts. This is between you and me, there's no appeal to outsiders.'

'There's nothing between you and me,' she said fiercely.

His eyes travelled over her slowly. 'Except a few clothes, and I could soon change that,' he agreed, tongue in cheek.

Her face flamed. 'I'd like to wipe that smug grin off your face!' she flung angrily.

'Try it,' he said softly.

She met his challenging eyes and her hand flew up. He caught it, forcing it down on to the grass without difficulty. She seethed, her eyes loathing him.

'Let me go!'

'So that you can smack my face? What do you take me for?'

Her lips parted, words of hatred and contempt on her tongue, but before she could say one of them he began to laugh, covering her mouth with his free hand, his eyes teasing her.

'Don't say it,' he said wickedly. 'Your eyes are very expressive, Leigh, and a lady should never use words like those, whatever the provocation.'

Against the strong, silencing hand her mouth made muffled sounds of bitter protest. She tried again to get up, but he leaned over her, his long, hard body easily defeating her attempt to escape.

He watched her, reading the blue blaze of her eyes with an amusement which seemed untouched by the scathing contempt she was throwing at him. Gradually the hard barrier across her mouth softened. The fingers began to slide gently over her face, outlining the cool, regular features, their tips smooth and caressing. Leigh was furious at the reaction her own body was giving him. She disliked and despised him, but she seemed unable to control the instinctive effect of his touch. There was some sort of chemical explosion which happened every time she set eyes on him. It had nothing to do with the emotions, she told herself contemptuously. It was purely physical, but potent, all the same. However she rationalised it to herself, she found herself, every time, the victim of the same violent upheaval, as though there was a flaw in her character, a hidden abyss from which these searing flames flew upwards in response to the presence of this man.

'If you promise to behave yourself I'll let you go,' he said softly. 'I want to talk to you. Will you swear not to bolt like a terrified doe if I let go of you?'

Her blue eyes surveyed him smoulderingly, then with a faint sigh she nodded.

He removed his hands, swinging away from her to sit

up, his arms laced around his knees, watching her.

Leigh sat up, instinctively tidying her hair and the dark brown silk of her dress. His lazy glance followed every movement, and she became intensely aware of the way he was watching her. Turning her head, she gave him her coldest glance.

'Well?'

'My secretary is leaving to get married,' he said. 'I want you to take the job.'

The casual statement took her breath away, then she gasped aloud. 'Why, you ...' She closed her lips on the insult she was about to fling at him. After a pause she said stiffly, 'I have a very good job, Mr Hume. I have no intention of changing it.'

'What's your salary?' he asked in an unmoved tone.

Tightly, she told him.

'I'll double it,' he said, watching her face.

She looked at him, taken aback and suddenly wildly angry. 'You don't honestly expect me to take the job, do you? I can imagine just what functions your secretary would be expected to fulfil, and believe me, I've no intention of so much as considering taking an offer like that! The fact that you've made it is sufficiently insulting.' She scrambled to her feet and faced him as he joined her. 'Goodbye, Mr Hume. In future will you please leave me alone? I'm not the sort of girl you're looking for.'

'You've no idea what sort of girl you are, Leigh,' he drawled mockingly. 'There are going to be no goodbyes between us, so don't waste your energy in running. You're going to need every ounce of it in the hand to hand fighting.'

Her face was washed with bright colour, her eyes vivid as summer lightning in her face. 'You vain, egotistical swine ... someone ought to teach you a lesson you richly deserve!'

He grinned. 'You can try, Leigh,' he said in his lazily assured voice.

For a wild second Leigh was on the point of acknowledging that she was tempted to accept his gauntlet of challenge. It would be richly satisfying to take him up on that dare. But something buried deep inside her head warned her of the danger of the gamble. She was not quite sure she could win. Mattieson Hume was too dangerous to tangle with, and she was afraid of the outcome.

'I can't be bothered,' she said, lifting her sleek head with a shrug of her shoulders. 'You aren't worth it.'

As she turned to walk away he fell in step beside her, his hand under her elbow, although she tried to pull out of his grasp.

'I'll drive you back to the hotel,' he said.

'I would rather walk. I wanted to do some shopping.' She halted to look at him directly. 'Please, will you leave me alone? You're ruining my morning.'

He looked at her through his dark lashes, a calculating look on his attractive face. 'This job is a serious offer, Leigh,' he began.

'I know what it is,' she said through tight lips. 'Don't repeat the suggestion or I'll do something we'll both regret.'

'I want a secretary, not a mistress,' he said flatly. 'If you want a reference for me, ask my previous secretary ... she's worked for me for three years and she knows me very well. I've always had a very smooth working relationship with her.'

'I'm sure you have,' she said bitingly.

'You wouldn't say it like that if you knew her,' he said, his voice crisp. 'She's a very nice girl. I give you my word of honour there's never been anything between us that I wouldn't want her future husband to know about.'

His tone was convincing, but she looked at him scathingly. 'Maybe that's true, but your behaviour ever since we met hasn't given me the impression that I can rely on the same decency.'

A wicked light gleamed in his grey eyes. 'Surely you have enough trust in your own ability to hold me at arm's length, Leigh, to take the risk?'

She knew she did not have any trust in her ability to keep him at arm's length, but she also knew the danger of admitting as much, so she said coldly, 'I prefer to stay where I am. I wouldn't be able to see much of my fiancé if I was in London while he was in Leicester.'

'On the other hand, think how much you could save,' he pointed out softly.

'I can imagine what Phil would say if I told him you'd offered me that sort of money,' she burst out. 'His suspicions would be along the same lines as mine, I imagine, and he wouldn't let me accept.'

He grinned. 'Oh, I don't know. London salaries are much higher than those in the provinces, and I'm the head of a very large organisation. The salary I'm offering you isn't wildly above the norm for the sort of position you would be occupying. My present secretary gets a salary just a fraction less than that, in fact.'

She was surprised, her eyes widening at the information.

He laughed. 'Disappointed? Would you rather believe I'm offering to buy other services than your secretarial skills?'

'You can get someone much better for the job in London,' she said, ignoring his suggestion. 'I'm hardly qualified.'

'On the contrary, you are very qualified,' he said blandly. 'You are distinctly lovely to look at, very efficient, I would guess, you don't see me in a glamorous light and you wouldn't make a nuisance of yourself.'

The statements took her breath away. She stared at him.

He began to laugh again at her expression of incredulity. 'I can see you have no idea of the problems confronting an eligible bachelor when it comes to appointing a secretary,' he said with a grin. 'Being a normal male, I like to have attractive girls working for me—they're nice to look at and they please my visitors. But if I get a girl who has her sights set on becoming Mrs Hume I'm in dead trouble. From time to time I've made a mistake, and got a girl who was blinded by the glamour of working for me.'

'How awkward for you,' said Leigh in mock sympathy, her eyes scornful.

He looked amused. 'Do you expect me to be unaware of the glamour of my job? I run a glossy business. The media have a deceptive brilliance to outsiders. Now you, Leigh, I suspect, have no romantic image of my world.'

'No, none,' she snapped.

'Which makes you an excellent candidate for the job,' he went on blandly. 'I wouldn't need to be wary of finding myself being pursued, would I, Leigh?'

'No, you wouldn't,' she said, her colour high, her eyes blazing. 'Never in a million years.'

'As I suspected,' he agreed silkily. 'We would make a good team. You're safely engaged to another man and you're not likely to be tempted by the idea of becoming my wife.'

'I wouldn't touch you with a bargepole,' she said tensely.

He looked amused. 'I wouldn't put it quite like that,' he said very softly, and suddenly her heart was racing wildly.

Turning away, she moved towards the car, her slender body stiff. He caught up with her, eyeing her face with grey eyes which read the anger tautening her skin.

'The work would be much more interesting than working for a provincial solicitor,' he said.

'I don't want the job,' she snapped.

'We could at least discuss it . . .'

'No!'

He opened the car and she got into the passenger seat. He slid behind the wheel and glanced at her averted profile.

'Will you please take me back to the hotel?' she asked through tight lips.

'Just as you like,' he said, shrugging. The engine started and they drove away through the wrought iron gates of the park into the thick traffic. Leigh was still bitterly angry at his suggestion. He might pretend he had other reasons for the offer he had made her, but his behaviour towards her so far had made it obvious that to accept a job which entailed spending hours alone with him in an office would be tantamount to staying in Bluebeard's castle. She did not trust him. She thought of her cousin's pale, broken little face, and anger darkened her blue eyes. He was completely ruthless in his pursuit of what he wanted. No doubt if Ann had slept with him the first night he took her out he would never have asked her out again. It was only the girl's loving innocence which had prevented him from pressing home his advantage. Even Mattieson Hume could not have failed to read the gentle innocence in Ann's soft eyes.

Calmly, he said, 'I think you're making a mistake, Leigh. You and I would suit each other very well. Beneath that elegant exterior you're as tough as leather, aren't you? I understand and respect the ruthless drive your fiancé fails to notice in you. I admit I was tempted to knock you off your pedestal—the sight of you aroused the iconoclastic impulse in me. Your fiancé may be happy to kneel and worship at the shrine, but adoration isn't my style. I'm offering you mutual equality, not worship.'

'I both love and respect Phil,' she said grittily.

'Just not true,' he retorted. 'How can you really respect a man who jumps when you crook your little finger? A woman of your intelligence needs a stronger opposition than that.' He shrugged easily. 'I can only suspect you like being the stronger partner of the two. Maybe Phil is what you want, a man who can always be dominated and manipulated.'

'I do not manipulate him!' she exclaimed, stung.

'Of course you do,' he said impatiently. 'It was as plain as daylight the first time I set eyes on you. I watched you operate from a distance and I was half irritated, half impressed by the way you handled him. When he got really upset you kissed him and that little peck was enough to make him happy again, wasn't it? You're a very clever angler, Leigh. You know how to reel the fish in with the minimum of effort.'

'Stop talking about me like that!' she snapped. 'That may be how you behave with the women in your life, but I'm not you.'

'We're more alike than you'll admit,' he told her, his eyes on the road.

The statement had a curious effect on her. Her body seemed to burn with unexpected, blazing heat. She sat staring out of the window, fighting desperately against the emotions which were sending her blood racing round her body, her nerves jumping violently.

'You're ambitious, aren't you?' he asked, as if unaware of the effect of what he had said. 'If you work with me you'll be stretched to the limit, Leigh. It isn't an easy job. It demands a good brain, a cool head and a great deal of work. But it is rewarding.' He pulled up outside the hotel and looked round at her.

She had got herself partially under control again. She met his dissecting glance coolly.

'Not rewarding enough,' she said icily. 'I like to work for people I respect.'

He shrugged and leaned forward, releasing the door handle so that she could get out. 'A pity,' he said.

'Goodbye, Mr Hume,' her voice replied bitingly.

He laughed. 'You know me better than that, Leigh,' he said, mockery in every line. 'I'll be seeing you.'

She slammed the door and walked into the hotel.

Lunching with Phil she looked at him, wondering angrily if there could be any truth in Mattieson Hume's remarks about the way she acted towards him. She had never seen herself in that light, nor had she regarded Phil as a man easy to manipulate. Their eyes met and he smiled at her lovingly. She returned the smile and looked back at her plate. The truth behind those bitter, stinging accusations Mattieson Hume had made was that Phil loved her more than she loved him, and it was that gap which made the difference.

When one person was more deeply in love, it put them at a disadvantage. She was anxious as she admitted the fact. There was one who kissed, while the other merely accepted the kisses. Phil was suffering from the weakness of loving her more than she could love him.

They talked while they drank their coffee, and he eyed her in some anxiety. 'You're so subdued, darling. Are you bored?'

She looked at him directly. 'No, just thinking.'

'About what?'

'Us,' she admitted.

His eyes were grave. 'What about us, Leigh?'

'You were right when you said the other night that it would be madness to get married while we were not sure,' she said huskily.

His face whitened and he put down his cup. 'Leigh, I ...'

'Please, let me finish,' she said quickly. 'Phil, I've been unfair to you. When you asked me to marry you, I accepted because I was fond of you and liked being with you, but I never felt the same way as you do ... I knew that, even then. I didn't think it mattered. I thought we would work it out somehow.'

'And now?' he asked, as if he could hardly phrase the question through his white lips.

She met his eyes. 'If we marry as we are, something disastrous may happen. Love has to be equal. You'll begin to resent and hate me if we get married as we planned. I think you should accept that job in Saudi Arabia. It will give us a breathing space, time for me to work out whether or not I love you the way you want me to.'

He stared at her, his face shaken. 'Leigh, if I leave you for six months someone else will take you away from me.'

She shook her head. 'I promise I'll only let that happen if I fall in love myself, and, Phil, that could happen even if we married today. If I was going to fall in love you couldn't stop it, could you? Better for us to find out before we get married than afterwards.'

'Oh, God, I should have held my tongue,' he said to himself. 'I put these ideas into your head, after the wedding, didn't I? I've dug my own grave.'

She put her hand on his gently, shaking her head. 'Sooner or later this would have had to happen because we both know that what you said is true. It isn't fair to you if I marry you without being able to respond as passionately as you want me to.'

His mouth was wry with pain. 'Half a loaf is better than no bread,' he sighed.

'Not always,' said Leigh. Mattieson Hume had opened

her eyes to the truth about the relationship with Phil, but he had also opened her eyes to her own needs and feelings. She detested and despised him, but he only had to touch her for her whole body to burn into terrifying life. Phil had never done that to her. She suspected miserably that when she was with Phil he was feeling very much the same way she had felt in Mattieson Hume's arms today. The thought of marrying him, knowing how little she could give him which would ease the pain of his desire, was horrifying. Her reaction to Mattieson Hume might only be a physical, chemical reaction, but it was monumental, and she guessed that to offer a substitute for that to Phil would be nothing short of cruel. Phil had a right to know what it was like to be given back the love he offered.

Anything less would be immoral.

Phil gave a long sigh. 'Are you trying to let me down gently, Leigh?' he asked after a pause.

Their eyes met. She smiled at him ruefully. 'I'm giving us both a chance to think more clearly,' she said. 'Away from me, you'll be able to see the situation as it is.'

'And our engagement?' he asked roughly. 'Does it still stand?'

She nodded. 'Until you ask for your ring back, Phil.'

'I won't do that,' he said.

Leigh did not answer. Although she did not turn her head she had suddenly become aware that Mattieson Hume was on the other side of the dining-room; her ears had picked up the dark timbre of his voice, and she caught the silvery chime of laughter answering him. Her tense stiffness eased. He was with a woman. At least, she told herself, she could relax for the moment. If he was with someone he would be no threat to her.

Phil glanced at his watch. 'Time for the second session,' he said huskily. 'I'll have to go.'

Leigh stood up. 'I'll walk with you,' she offered. 'I think I'll take a look around this part of London this afternoon.'

He was looking rather shaken, she realised, glancing at him in affectionate sympathy. Her hand slid into his and his fingers gripped it tightly. She pressed her shoulder against him, murmuring gently, 'Don't look so grim, darling. Six months isn't a lifetime.'

'It is when you want someone as badly as I want you,' he muttered under his breath.

As they walked out of the dining-room she was deeply tempted to look round. Curiosity about Mattieson Hume's female companion was eating at her. But she controlled the impulse, concentrating instead upon Phil. As they left the hotel they ran into Fiona and Jefferson, who hailed them enthusiastically. They walked along together, talking, then Leigh left them and went for a long stroll around the London streets.

She returned to the hotel later in the afternoon, and went up to her room to have a shower and change for the evening.

She was just towelling herself when the telephone rang. She answered it, the towel wrapped around her loosely, and felt an electric shock of surprise as she recognised the voice on the other end.

'Where have you been all afternoon?' it asked directly without identifying itself.

For a second or two Leigh breathed thickly, then she said in a pretence of bewilderment. 'Who is speaking, please?'

There was a soft laughter. 'Come down to the bar and have a drink with me, Leigh.'

'I've just got out of the shower,' she said tightly. 'I'm afraid I shan't be dressed for some time. Goodbye.'

She had not expected him to accept her refusal, but to

her surprise the phone went dead. She looked at it, then shrugged and went back into the bathroom. Finishing the process of drying herself, she slipped into a loose white wrap and began to lay out her clothes on the bed. When the door opened she turned, her heart in her mouth, and looked across the room at him with a stunned apprehension.

'Get out,' she said shakily. 'Get out before I ring the hotel management.'

'You left your door on the latch,' he said softly. 'I thought you meant me to come in.'

She remembered then that she had done so when she first came in because the floor maid had said she wanted to take away the contents of the waste paper basket, and Leigh did not want to have to leave the shower to let her into the room. But she gave him a frigid look. 'You knew perfectly well I wasn't expecting you.'

'Then you're more stupid than I'd thought, because the moment you told me you were just out of the shower you must have known it would bring me up here,' he said audaciously, taking her breath away.

'Why, you . . .'

'You said it deliberately,' he murmured, his grey eyes moving slowly down the length of her body. 'My God, Leigh, even my vivid imagination hadn't conjured up the way you look now.'

She backed, her eyes held by the darkening insistence of his stare. 'No,' she said weakly as he reached her.

'Yes, Leigh,' he whispered under his breath as his hands moved towards her.

She shuddered, backing, and overbalanced as the back of her knees met the edge of the bed. She fell, a cry of fear on her lips, and he joined her, holding her half naked body under him by the weight of his own. For a few seconds they stared at each other. Her breathing was erratic and painful. Then he made a rough sound under his breath and began to kiss her, and all rational thought vanished from her head.

She was so dazed by the hot pressure of his long kisses that she did not even notice when he shrugged out of his jacket and threw his tie down on to the floor. Her eyes shut, she arched in bitter pleasure as his hands began to move over her. Her fingers were shaking as they ran over his hard chest, hearing his heart beat under them. He kissed her throat, his lips silkily intimate as they ventured behind her ears and stroked back stray strands of hair from her face. Leigh's hands moved behind his head, digging into his black hair, then jerked his head down towards her to meet the seeking invitation of her parted lips.

His mouth explored hers sensuously, one hand under her tilted head, his fingers stroking along her nape. Leigh had lost all sense of time and place. She was utterly abandoned to the deep erotic sensations he was arousing in her, her mind subjugated to the demands of her body.

A stifled sound woke them both out of their concentration on each other. Blindly Leigh turned her head on the pillow, her eyes reluctantly opening, and felt shock run through her as she saw Phil in the doorway, staring in white-faced incredulity at them.

She was unable to move or speak. The silence seemed to stretch interminably. Then Phil turned on his heel and went out.

'I must have forgotten to lock the door again,' Mattieson Hume said in a dry voice.

She looked round at him, her blue eyes wide in her white face. Her glance saw him as Phil must have seen him—his shirt undone, his hair ruffled, quite obviously a man who had been making passionate love.

Bitterly, she said, 'Did you plan that, Mr Hume? I

hope you're satisfied with yourself after this!'

He looked at her in sudden grimness. 'It takes two, Leigh,' he said directly.

She lost her pallor in a rush of hot scarlet. His eyes moved over her, narrowed and wry. 'There was no fight this time, was there?'

She squirmed in distasteful realisation of what Phil had seen as he looked at them. Mattieson Hume with jacket and tie discarded and shirt undone lying on the bed with her, her hair loose, her body totally responsive in his arms, the thin white wrap barely concealing the fact of her nakedness beneath.

Sickened, she whispered, 'He must have thought I ... we ...'

'He thought we were doing just what we were doing,' the hard voice commented.

She shook her head, shuddering. 'No!'"

His fingers tightened around her face, holding her head so that she could not look away. 'If he'd walked in here in another ten minutes he would have seen something that would have destroyed your pedestal even more finally,' he told her ruthlessly. 'And if you're honest with yourself, you know it.'

'You swine,' she whispered shakily.

'Why? Because I'm telling the truth? Just before he came in here, you were mine to take, and you know it.'

She slapped his face so hard her palm stung. He didn't move or react in any way. For a moment he merely stared down at her.

'Next time you hit me, Leigh, I'll hit you back,' he said at last, his voice flinty. 'This time I'll let you off with a warning.'

'Get out,' she said hoarsely. 'Get out of my room and out of my life, and stay away from me!'

He smiled sardonically. Getting off the bed, he picked

up his jacket and tie and did up his shirt, his hands quite cool and steady as they fastened the buttons.

Leigh watched bitterly as he strolled towards the door. He halted to look back at her, his grey eyes insolently running over her. 'I'll be seeing you,' he said softly, then he walked out of the room.

CHAPTER FOUR

WHEN Mattieson Hume had gone Leigh dressed rapidly and went up to the next floor to see Phil. While dressing, she had been tempted to write him a letter and pack, leaving without seeing him, but her innate sense of self-respect made her realise that that was a cowardly way out of the situation. She had to see him face to face.

He opened the door at her knock and looked at her, his brown eyes dull.

Silently he stood back and she walked into the room, her blonde head bent. For the first time in her life Leigh was aware of a feeling of bitter humility. She had hurt Phil deeply, and she despised herself for it.

Phil stood with his hands in his pockets, staring at the floor. She looked at him, wincing at the lines of suffering on his face.

'I'm sorry, Phil,' she whispered unsteadily.

There was a silence. 'You could have told me,' he said in a totally unfamiliar voice, sharpened by anguish. 'You didn't have to be so devious.'

'Devious?' she repeated, frowning.

He lifted his head then, his eyes stabbing her. 'You

were sending me off to Saudi Arabia to get me out of the way, weren't you, Leigh? If you wanted him why didn't you just tell me?'

She swallowed, shuddering. 'It isn't like that ... you're wrong, Phil, quite wrong. I was honest about that.' She bit her lip. 'It's true that the way ... the way I feel about ...' Her voice broke off, and she made a gesture of impotence. 'Phil, I don't want to feel like that. I just couldn't help it. I wasn't sending you away because I wanted him. I just saw that if he could affect me like that, it would be very wrong for me to go on with the wedding plans. As far as he's concerned, I hope I never set eyes on him again. I detest him!'

Phil stared at her, his brown eyes probing her pale face. 'You detest him,' he repeated oddly, his voice shaking. 'Oh, God, Leigh, do you think I'm blind? It only needed one look to know exactly how you feel about him.'

She flushed deeply. 'Feel isn't the right word,' she said, angry humility in her face. 'Emotion doesn't come into it.'

'If I hadn't walked in then you would have been in bed with him by now,' Phil said tightly.

She lowered her head, not denying it. 'I don't like the way I've behaved,' she said. 'You have every right to be furious with me. I was going to go home, leaving you a letter, but I couldn't be such a coward. I'm not asking you to forgive me, I just wanted to give you the chance to say what you want to say.'

There was a curious silence, and she slowly looked up. He was staring at her, his eyes narrowed. A curious smile quivered on his mouth. 'I'm sorry I called you devious, Leigh,' he said wryly. 'You're not, are you?'

She sighed. Taking off her engagement ring, she held it out to him. Phil glanced at it, shaking his head.

'You said you would wear it until I asked for it back,' he reminded her.

'That was before ...'

'All that has changed is that I've discovered you can be knocked off balance sexually, Leigh,' he said, his tone odd. 'I've often wondered if you were basically immune to feelings like that. I'm sick with jealousy because it took another man to show me that you aren't, but I still want to hold you if I can.'

She backed, shaking her head. 'No, Phil, it wouldn't be fair.'

'You say you never hope to see him again,' Phil reminded her. 'It isn't a serious relationship, is it?' His eyes narrowed and dark colour came surging into his face. 'You haven't been to bed with him already, have you?'

'No,' she said thickly.

'And you're sure you aren't in love with him?'

'I hate him,' she said tensely.

'Then keep the ring, Leigh. If you want to give it back to me when I return, then I'll accept it as final. But in the meantime, will you keep it?'

She frowned. 'It wouldn't be sensible, Phil. How can you suggest such a thing after ...'

'You lost your head when a sophisticated man made a violent pass at you,' Phil said drily. 'You remember what an effect he had on your cousin. I expect he does this sort of thing all the time. If I'd known that that was all it was, I'd have punched his face at the time, but I was too shaken by what I saw, and I thought you had to be in love with him.' His face was tight with pain. 'I've been afraid you'd fall for someone else ever since we met, Leigh. I thought this was it ...'

She sighed deeply. 'You had every right to be angry. Don't be so understanding—I don't deserve it.'

Phil laughed angrily. 'My God, you ask for trouble, Leigh!' He took her by the elbows and drew her towards him, looking down into her face, his eyes feverish. 'Ever since I walked into that damned room I've been seeing visions of you that have driven me almost out of my mind. For the first time since I met you, I saw you without that cool mask you wear, and then it had to be for another man.'

'I'm sorry,' she said weakly.

'Sorry!' His laughter was grim. She saw a look come blazing into his brown eyes and pulled away, but his grip was tightening. He almost threw her bodily on to the bed and joined her, his hands cruelly holding her down, while he found her mouth, his desperate hunger making him immune to her struggles. Leigh sensed that for the first time in their relationship Phil was out of her control. Whenever he tried to make love to her in the past he had been holding himself on a leash. Now the leash had snapped, and his kisses savaged her, his hands moving over her with mounting eagerness. For some time she resisted him, but her movements only inflamed him, so she gave up the attempt to fight, and lay quiescent under his passion, allowing him to do as he pleased.

He had unzipped her dress, pushing it down over her shoulders, his lips covering her bare shoulders with kisses which burned her skin. When his face moved down to the deep white hollow between her breasts she felt him trembling. 'Oh, God, Leigh,' he whispered ardently. 'I want you so much.'

She was so moved with pity that she stroked his head, not finding the way he was touching her unpleasant. He lifted his head, his breath coming harshly, and looked into her eyes.

Gently she looked back, her blue eyes compassionate.

Phil closed his eyes briefly, a spasm of agony crossing

his face. Then he sat up, his back to her.

'It isn't any good, is it?' he asked her drily. 'You just don't feel that way for me at all.'

'I'm sorry, Phil,' she said heavily.

'For God's sake, stop saying that!'

'I don't know what else to say,' she admitted.

'I'm only fooling myself by hoping that after six months you might have discovered you loved me,' he said. 'I doubt if you ever felt anything more than fondness for me.'

'I do love you in a way,' she said.

'Like a brother,' he said ironically.

'Oh, Phil,' she groaned, her voice filled with unshed tears, 'I didn't want to hurt you.'

He stood up, straightening his shoulders. 'At least we aren't married,' he said grimly. 'I should be grateful for that small mercy.'

She took off her ring again and laid it on his bed. He looked at it with bitterness.

'I'll leave tonight,' she said quietly. 'I'll go and pack now.'

Phil didn't answer, staring at her without saying a word, flame in the centre of his brown eyes.

Leigh slowly left the room and returned to her own. When she had packed she went down and paid her hotel bill. The porter got her a taxi and she drove away from the hotel feeling drained and sick.

When she reached home that night her mother looked at her in puzzled enquiry. 'Why are you back early? Is something wrong?'

Leigh held out her naked hand. 'My engagement is over, Mother. I don't want to talk about it, though. Will you tell Dad?'

Mrs West raised an eyebrow. 'Is that all we're going to be told, Leigh?' She had her daughter's colouring and bone structure, her body elegant in the dark dress she wore, her silvered hair worn in a smooth chignon at the back of her head.

'There's nothing to discuss,' said Leigh, preparing to go to her room.

Her parents had never insisted on breaching her privacy. They were too busy running the family business, a small antique shop in Leicester, to interfere in Leigh's concerns, and she was grateful for the fact at the moment.

Over the next few days she had a difficult job in keeping her temper under the questions which were flung at her. Her broken engagement caused a good deal of speculation, and it irritated her that most of it should be damaging to Phil. Gossip relayed to her by her mother was already putting the blame at his door.

'Is it true that Phil has a girl at his firm, Leigh?' her mother asked her. 'Some redhead who went to London too? Did you find them together? Is that what happened?'

'No,' Leigh said tersely. 'It's all lies.'

But she did not tell her mother the truth; it was too embarrassing to discuss. That evening she decided to go to the cinema. She needed to get out of the house for a while. Walking down the main street, she found herself face to face with Phil. He looked at her uncertainly.

She flushed and would have passed without a word, but he halted her.

'Surely we can talk to each other, Leigh?' he asked ruefully.

She glanced at him nervously. 'How are you, Phil?'

'Apparently my reputation is sky high at the moment,' he said sarcastically.

She flushed, even more dramatically, and looked away. 'I didn't start that stupid sordid story,' she muttered. 'I refused to say a word. I suppose people just filled in the gap with their own version.'

'I'm grateful to you,' he said, in the same voice.

'Don't be angry, Phil,' she said pleadingly.

'Angry?' His voice held an unpleasant note. 'Why should I be angry? The men in my office think I'm a gay Lothario who got caught out, and they envy me my supposed conquests, even while they're laughing at the thought that you found me out. Even Fiona seems more flattered than annoyed.' He gave her a grim smile. 'It seems her reputation has gone up like a rocket since it got round that she stole me from you.' His eyes were ironic. 'Oddly enough I think you've got the most unenviable position of the three of us, Leigh. Everyone is sorry for you, but laughing behind your back.'

She met his deliberately taunting stare. 'I know,' she said quietly. 'And not even behind my back all the time.'

'Poor Leigh,' he said coldly. 'Never mind, it's a nine-day wonder. I'm leaving for Saudi Arabia this weekend, and it will blow over once I've gone. My boss has agreed to send me at once. He's heard the story, of course, and he thinks I want to escape before Fiona tries to force me to marry her.'

Leigh looked at him through her lowered lashes. 'I'm sorry, Phil,' she murmured.

Footsteps behind them slowed. She glanced round and saw some vaguely recognisable faces, her colour rising. She turned back towards Phil. 'I must go,' she said nervously.

He held her wrist before she could move, nodding over her shoulder to the trio of people behind her. 'Hallo,' he said briefly. They chorused and moved on, glancing back with eager curiosity towards them. They were all from his firm, and were dying to know what he was saying to her.

Phil looked down at her, his mouth set hard in his angry face. 'You might at least kiss me goodbye, Leigh,' he said coldly. 'At least it will give the gossip something to feed on for a while ... rumours of a reconciliation could fly around until they realise I've gone.'

'Don't, Phil,' she winced, hearing the bitterness in his voice.

He bent and kissed her hard, his mouth cruel. For a moment she stood unresisting, then he pushed her away and walked in the opposite direction very fast.

The next morning she was surprised and baffled to receive a typewritten letter from London. Her mother and father had already left for their shop. She opened the envelope and began to read it, her frown growing, until a sudden wave of angry temper swept over her. It was a formal letter thanking her for her application for the position as secretary and inviting her for an interview on the following day, as she had been shortlisted among the other applicants. She read the hard, black signature several times with eyes that felt hot as though someone had rubbed sand into them.

For a moment she was on the point of tearing the letter up, then a surge of bitter rage seemed to envelop her. She walked like a zombie to the telephone and rang her boss, asking for the day off for private reasons. He was oddly sympathetic, urging her to take the following day off too. 'We aren't that busy, Miss West. I'm sure we can manage without you for a little while.'

Only afterwards did it occur to her that he imagined that her supposed discovery of Phil's infidelity was the cause of her absence. The irony made her smile savagely.

She went back upstairs and chose her favourite dress to wear. Black, rather sleek-fitting, it emphasised her blonde fragility and self-assurance. She felt capable of defying Mattieson Hume as she left the house, and during the long train ride to London she was mentally rehearsing the scene in his office. She varied the synopsis from time to time, but one action remained each time—

she would tear up his damned insolent letter and throw the pieces into his face before she walked out.

When she found the offices of World Gazette she stood outside for a long time, staring up at the rows of windows with a sinking heart. She had been buoyed up throughout her journey by the thought of violent action. Now she felt her courage fade.

But she stiffened her backbone and went into the foyer. A porter in a gold-buttoned uniform gave her an encouraging smile. 'Can I help you, miss?'

'I want to see Mr Hume,' she said huskily. She showed him her letter. 'I can't keep the appointment tomorrow.'

He looked at her. 'Miss West,' he said, reading the letter. He was a man in his early sixties, a wiry, friendly-faced man with grey hair. 'If you'll take the lift to the top floor, miss, you'll find yourself right opposite the door to Mr Hume's office. Miss Harrison will deal with the problem.'

Leigh went up in the lift and stepped out into a long, cream-painted corridor. She tapped on the door opposite and heard a voice invite her inside. Nervously she looked at the girl facing her.

'Miss Harrison?'

The other girl smiled in a friendly fashion. She was extremely attractive, her tall, rounded body graceful in a black skirt and white blouse, her chestnut hair enlivened by golden light which shone in the sunlight streaming through the window behind her. Brown eyes smiled at Leigh.

'You're Miss West? Sam rang up that you were on your way.'

'Sam?' Leigh frowned.

'Our porter. Nobody comes in or goes out of the building unless Sam notices it,' said Miss Harrison. 'If you're going to work here you're going to see a lot of Sam.' She smiled again, displaying even white teeth. 'Mr Hume will see you right away. You're lucky—he thought you might arrive early as it was such short notice, and he cancelled some of his appointments for today.' Her brown eyes danced. 'Believe me, he needs a good secretary. He works like a slave and you have to keep an eye on him to make sure he doesn't overdo it.' She leaned forward, depressing a button on the console. 'Miss West is here, Mr Hume.'

'Send her in,' said the maddening voice, the familiarity of it altered a little by the medium.

'Through that door,' Miss Harrison said calmly.

Leigh walked through the door and closed it behind her. Across a large, pleasantly furnished office she saw him lounging in his chair, his jacket open, his shirt unbuttoned at the throat, a gleam of mockery in his grey eyes.

At the sight of him her rage was so fierce she could barely move or speak. Forcing herself forward, she walked to the desk and looked at him. With a frantic gesture she tore the letter across, ripped it to pieces and threw the pieces into his face.

He laughed softly. 'I bet you've been planning that little piece of histrionics ever since you opened the envelope,' he said.

The shrewdness of the reply inflamed her. 'How dared you send me that letter? You know very well I didn't apply for the job, and you know I don't want to be interviewed.'

'But you're here,' he pointed out, his mouth humorous.

'Only to tell you what I think of you,' she said bitingly.

He leaned back, his eyes filled with that secret mockery. 'I know what you think of me, Leigh. Sit down. You might as well hear the details of the job.'

'I wouldn't take a job working for you if you offered me four times what I'm getting now,' she said.

'You aren't worth four times what you're getting now,' he said wryly. 'I'm offering you a salary commensurate with your ability.'

'I'd rather work for nothing than work for you,' she snapped, turning on her heel.

He was on his feet and beside her before she had taken more than a few steps. She wrenched her arm out of his hand. 'Let me go, damn you!'

'You came, Leigh,' he said tersely. 'I knew you'd come.'

There was a second's silence while they stared at each other. She was so furious that she flung her hand up to hit him, but he caught it in his own, making her wince at the strength of his grip.

'I told you last time that if you hit me I'd hit you back,' he said. 'I meant it. Now, sit down.'

He pushed her into a chair and sat down on the edge of the desk nearby, staring at her. Seeing the way his eyes were fixed on her left hand she pushed it down into her skirt.

'Too late, Leigh,' he said drily. 'I'd already noticed it. I gather the engagement is off.'

'Thanks to you,' she said bitterly.

'You were never in love with him,' he shrugged.

She got up rigidly, facing him with burningly angry eyes. 'I only came here to tell you what a despicable, conceited swine you are. I have no intention of taking that job and I never want to hear from you again!'

She turned to leave, feeling him move from his casual position on the desk. The door was abruptly flung open at that second and a girl walked into the room, her eyes swinging curiously from Leigh to Mattieson Hume.

'Matt darling,' she pouted. 'Your secretary tried to put me off, but I have to talk to you.' She ignored Leigh, moving to his side, putting a graceful arm around his neck, gazing into his eyes. 'You are going to the party tonight, aren't you? You haven't answered your invitation yet, and Mother wondered if you were coming ...'

He gazed back at her, his grey eyes lightly amused, a faint smile on his hard mouth. 'Of course I'm coming, Cathy. If you'd rung me, I would have told you that. I'm very busy interviewing today, so I'm afraid you can't stop now. Run along, darling, and I'll see you tonight, I promise.'

She made a little face. She was about twenty, Leigh decided, watching her curiously. The curly black hair and huge green eyes gave her skin a delicate transparency which made her appear younger than she was, but she wore expensive, high fashion clothes which compensated for that.

So this was Cathy Lord, Leigh thought wryly. No wonder poor little Ann had no chance with him. What competition! Every glossy, spoilt inch of her was devastatingly attractive, and her confident, sweet smile at Mattieson Hume hinted at a very intimate relationship.

Realising that now was her chance to escape while his attention was distracted, she began to move discreetly towards the open door, but his hand snaked out and caught her by the wrist, halting her.

'Don't leave just yet, Miss West,' he said coolly. 'I haven't finished outlining the details of the job.'

Cathy Lord turned to eye her, taking in Leigh's cold, tense blonde beauty, the sleek black dress which fitted her like a second skin, the graceful elegance of her rigidly held body.

Leigh sensed that the younger girl was jealously apprehensive as her glance slid over her. Icily, she said, 'I think we'd said all we have to say, Mr Hume. I don't think this job would suit me at all.'

Cathy Lord took in the chilly tone, the frozen expression of the blue eyes with a satisfied expression.

'Nevertheless,' said Mattieson Hume with a bite, 'I still have a few things to say to you.' He looked at Cathy. 'Would you mind, darling? I'll see you later, I promise.'

Cathy gave Leigh a little glance, then shrugged. She moved to the door, then looked back, taking in the way Mattieson Hume still gripped Leigh's wrist. A frown wrinkled her forehead. 'Could I just have a private word first?' she asked him.

He hesitated, his face slightly grim. Releasing Leigh, he walked to the door. Cathy whispered to him, perfectly audibly, 'I don't like her. Don't give her the job.'

For a few seconds Mattieson Hume stared down into the big green eyes. He smiled, all his charm coming into play. 'Minx,' he whispered back, slapping her lightly on her bottom. 'You leave me to manage my office, if you don't mind.'

Leigh could feel Cathy's jealousy as if it was visible. The green eyes surveyed her sulkily, then the girl went out of the room, slamming the door behind her.

Mattieson Hume leant on the closed door, his arms folded, and stared at Leigh. She thought angrily of Ann. He had a way of handling young girls so that they were weakly adoring even while they could sense that he was beyond them. Cathy Lord was no Ann, though—she had a rich family to protect her interests. Remembering what Ann had said, it was clear that Mattieson Hume meant to marry the girl one day. She was the right sort of girl, from a wealthy background, beautiful and presentable. Leigh could tell by the way he had looked at her that he was not in love with her. He was indulgent, amused, flirtatious with her. But in that marriage he would be the dominant partner. She suddenly remembered that he had accused her of preferring to be the one who dominated in a relationship, and told her that they were the same. If she had married Phil, she admitted grimly, he might have been right. When one person loved so much more than the other they were in a very weak position. In a way, she felt sorry for Cathy Lord.

'Have dinner with me tonight,' he said now, his tone careful.

'You're going to a party, remember,' she pointed out coldly.

He shrugged. 'I'll turn up late.'

Her mouth was sardonic. 'Not on my account, please.'

He studied her, his eyes attempting to get past the cold mask of her features. 'What sort of effect did the news of your broken engagement have at home? It must have caused some talk, I imagine.'

She met his gaze ironically. 'Both Phil and I refused to discuss it, so the gossips made up their own story.'

'Which was?'

'That I'd caught Phil with Fiona and broken the engagement out of jealous rage,' she said drily.

He lifted a dark brow. 'So you got all the sympathy? How unfair on Phil.'

'He seems quite flattered,' she said lightly. 'It hasn't done his reputation among the men he works with any harm at all.'

He grinned. 'What about your reputation?' he asked.

'I'm cast in the role of the deserted woman,' she said, her blue eyes cool. 'There's been some laughter and a great deal of snide comment.'

He gave her a curious little glance. 'That stings, does it? I'm surprised you don't want to get away from all the talk, then.'

'Phil says it's a nine-day wonder and will blow over,' she shrugged.

He moved away from the door. 'You've been seeing him?' There was a rasp in his voice. 'Hasn't the man any pride? Has he suggested you get engaged again?'

Leigh backed before his advance until she stood

against the desk. 'He's going to Saudi Arabia for six months,' she said tartly.

He stared into her cold eyes. 'You would enjoy working here, Leigh,' he said quietly. 'At least let Miss Harrison explain the work to you. Think about it.'

She frowned at him. 'Why do you want me to take it? If you think that I . . .'

'I think you'll make a very useful secretary,' he said, cutting her off. 'I've given you my reasons. I have no intention of employing anyone who might try to trap me into marriage, and I'm pretty sure you wouldn't do that.'

'I don't want any sort of relationship with you,' she said bluntly, her voice stiff.

'Good,' he said at once. 'Cathy will be relieved about that.'

Her blue eyes lifted to his face. 'She won't be pleased if you give me the job,' she said.

He grinned. 'I thought you'd heard that. Cathy would be jealous if I employed any woman who didn't look like Dracula's mother, but I'll have no trouble persuading her to accept you.'

No, thought Leigh angrily. He would have no trouble talking Cathy Lord into anything. He was used to having things all his own way. She was under no illusions. He wanted her as his secretary because he intended to try to seduce her into a private relationship with him once she was constantly in his company. He had made his desire plain from the first moment they met. But Leigh had suddenly discovered a burning desire of her own—a wish to get her revenge on Mattieson Hume both for herself and for Ann. He had used his charm once too often. She had no intention of succumbing to it, as Ann had, and then finding herself thrown aside when she became an embarrassment.

He might be able to charm Cathy Lord into believing

that he was not interested in her for the moment, but one day, Leigh firmly decided, she would turn the tables on him with a vengeance. Sooner or later she would get the chance to ruin his chances of marrying Cathy Lord. If he had really loved the girl, she might not have thought of the idea, but she had felt a distinct prick of pity as she saw the young face jealously turned up towards him, her adoring emotions written on her pretty face. It would be a kindness to Cathy Lord to show her exactly what sort of man Mattieson Hume was now before she had tied herself to him for life. Cathy Lord had some of Ann's vulnerability. Under her sophisticated exterior she was very young and easily hurt.

'Mr Hume,' she said slowly.

'Matt,' he replied at once, watching her intently.

Her dark lashes flickered. She looked up at him through them, bitterly viewing his hard, handsome face. 'If I took this job there would be one condition,' she said.

'Which is?' he asked, staring at her.

Her lashes rose, revealing her icy blue eyes. 'This is a purely business relationship,' she said. 'If you attempt to alter that condition I shall leave at once.'

His mouth twisted. 'Agreed,' he said flatly.

They stared at each other. She knew in the centre of her being that he had no intention of keeping the promise he had just given, and he knew that she was aware of his unspoken reservation. A bitter challenge lit her eyes.

'I mean it,' she said. 'If you so much as touch me you'll regret it.'

'You've made yourself very clear, Leigh,' he said sardonically. 'I understand perfectly.'

He didn't understand at all, she thought grimly. When she laid down that condition she had known that if he did try to seduce her she would make it her business to be certain that Cathy Lord found out just what sort of man he was, and by forcing him to promise to keep his hands off her she had made it his own decision. If he broke his word, he would be bringing his punishment on his own head. If he kept it, she would say nothing and do nothing which would upset his plans for marrying the poor girl.

'So,' he said slowly, staring at her face with a faint frown. 'Is it a deal?'

She nodded, still half reluctant. She was not going to find it easy to work for him, but she had decided it was time someone taught him a long-needed lesson.

'It's a deal,' she said.

He moved round behind his desk and sat down, depressing a button on the console. 'Come in, Miss Harrison,' he said. He looked at Leigh. 'I'll leave you with her while she explains this job to you. She's leaving in two weeks. How soon can you start work?'

'I have to give a week's notice,' she said.

'Can you do that tomorrow? Then you could have a week working with her so that she could show you the ropes.'

'I think that will be possible,' she agreed.

Miss Harrison came into the room, smiling. He gave her a nod. 'I've just engaged Miss West as your replacement. She'll start here in a week's time.'

Miss Harrison smiled at Leigh. 'Good. I shall be able to help you through the first problems. I'm afraid there are quite a few of them in this job, not least Mr Hume himself.' Her friendly, teasing smile touched his face.

Leigh followed her out of the office and for the rest of the day she listened attentively while Miss Harrison dealt with a number of callers and queries. The work was complicated, largely concerned with personnel and management problems, and Leigh admired the way the other girl coped, so cheerfully and easily, with the various different situations she was called in to unravel.

At five-thirty, Miss Harrison sighed. 'Thank God another day's over! I love this job, but I'm looking forward to my marriage and the day when I start to·run my own home instead of an office.' She grinned at Leigh. 'My future husband works in Exeter, so after our marriage I shall get a job down there near our house. I would have stayed on here if he'd lived near London, but actually I think this job is just too demanding for a married woman. Some evenings I don't get away until late at night, and no husband would put up with that.' She looked at Leigh appraisingly. 'You're very pretty. I suppose there's a man in the background for you, too.'

Mattieson Hume had opened the door halfway through that remark. His dry, mocking smile touched Leigh's face. Before she could reply, he said, 'I'd like a few words with you, Miss West. Goodnight, Miss Harrison. You might as well get an early night for once.'

'Thank you,' Miss Harrison said eagerly. 'I'll be seeing you in a week, then, Miss West.'

Leigh smiled back at her. 'I'll look forward to that.'

'So shall I,' the other girl said, leaving in a hurry.

Mattieson Hume stood away from his door, waving Leigh into the room. She sat down near the desk, her slim legs crossing. He leaned on the desk, his eyes on the elegant, silk-clad calves.

'Where shall we eat tonight?' he asked casually.

She gave him a cold look. 'I'm getting a train back to Leicester at once.'

'You must eat before you go,' he said. 'Why not with me?'

Her brows rose. 'Have you forgotten our agreement?'

His mouth was ironic. 'Does it cover having dinner as well as trying to get you into bed, Leigh? It seems a rather wide agreement.'

She felt a hot flush in her face. 'It covers anything that entails a personal rather than a business relationship,' she said crisply.

'I see.' He folded his arms. There was an odd silence. Then he asked flatly, 'What happened between yourself and your fiancé, Leigh? What did he say to you?'

'That's none of your business,' she said tartly.

'I would have said it was very much my business,' he said. 'Did you run off back to Leicester right away and send him back his ring? Or did he insist on seeing you?'

'Neither,' she said. 'I went to his room after you'd gone and we talked it over.'

Incredulity darkened his eyes. 'You went to his room, then?'

'It was the only thing I could do,' she said, stiffening angrily. 'I'd hurt him. I couldn't just run off and avoid a scene because I couldn't face him.'

He stared at her intently. 'So what happened?'

'He was angry and hurt,' she said tightly. 'What do you expect? For God's sake, what's the point of this inquisition?'

His grey eyes probed her face. 'Was it painful?'

Her face was pale. 'Very,' she said tersely. 'Does that satisfy you, Mr Hume?'

'I'm trying to put myself into his place,' he said in flat tones. 'I was wondering what I would have done if I'd been him.'

Leigh looked at him in sudden curiosity. 'What would you have done?'

He looked oddly harsh, his face all angles, a hard shine in his grey eyes. 'I'd have taken you by force myself,' he said.

Her breath caught in her throat. A slow red swept up her face. His eyes sharply penetrated her features, reading her reaction.

She was trembling slightly, remembering Phil's bitter, passionate lovemaking and the despair with which he had recognised that he could not get her to respond as she had to Mattieson Hume.

The grey eyes narrowed in grim speculation. 'Is that what he felt like, Leigh?' he asked her.

She didn't reply, her flushed face tense.

Her silence answered for her. Mattieson Hume bent forward, his body as coiled with anger as a spring.

'What on earth possessed you to go to his room, you little fool? Haven't you any idea about men at all? What happened? Did he hurt you?'

She silently shook her head. 'Phil isn't you, Mr Hume. He was angry, but he isn't a savage.'

'He's a man, damn you. I could have predicted what would happen if you'd told me what you meant to do. I thought you'd run off back to Leicester. It never occurred to me that you'd do such a stupid thing.'

'I owe him that much,' she said passionately. 'I'm not a coward.'

'No,' he said wryly, his mouth twisting. 'It was brave of you, Leigh. But stupid. The poor devil was crazy about you.' Slowly his eyes moved over her. 'He must have had quite a shock.' The grey eyes lifted to her face, trying to read her expression.

'He was hurt,' she said huskily. 'I shall always feel guilty about what I did to him.' And what you did, she thought, her blue eyes icy as they looked at him.

'He would have been a damned sight more hurt if he'd married you and then discovered he couldn't make it with you,' he said.

Her eyes burned with humiliated rage, but she looked away. The unspoken rider hung on the air between them ... Phil could never have made her respond the way Mattieson Hume had done, and they both knew it.

She stood up. 'I don't wish to discuss the subject any longer,' she said coldly. 'I must go now. Goodnight, Mr Hume.'

'If you call me that in private one more time, Leigh, I'll shove the words down your beautiful throat,' he said between his teeth. 'My name is Matt. In future, you'll use it.'

'I prefer to keep our relationship as formal as possible, Mr Hume,' she said coldly.

His hands caught her by the shoulders, and he shook her savagely, a sudden blazing rage lighting his grey eyes. 'You stubborn, idiotic little fool, why the hell did you go to his room? He might have half killed you. What did he do, Leigh?' His hands tightened. 'Tell me. What happened in that room?'

She looked at him in baffled incredulity. 'You have no right to ask me, and I have no intention of telling you,' she said.

He made a harsh, angry sound of frustrated impotence. 'What happened was as much my doing as yours,' he said, after a pause, his eyes watching her. 'Surely I have a right to know what followed?'

She lifted her chin. 'Do you want a blow-by-blow account of how he raped me, Mr Hume?'

For a moment all the colour ebbed from his face and his grey eyes had a steely glare in them. There was silence between them. His hands tightened on her shoulders until they ate into her flesh like iron cords.

'Tell me the truth,' he said below his breath, his voice a harsh, dry thread of sound.

'You're hurting me,' she said, struggling against him.

'Keep still,' he said. 'The truth, Leigh. I'm going to have it if I keep you here all night.'

Her blue eyes duelled with the hard grey flint ones for a moment, then she felt her resistance draining. Huskily, she said, 'He ... tried to make love to me, but Phil is too decent to be capable of it. So he stopped.' Her face was bitter. 'Is that enough information for you? Or do you need to be told exactly what he did to me?'

He shook her almost absently, as if she were a naughty child. 'Be quiet, Leigh,' he said harshly. His eyes probed into her face. 'Why did you let me think he'd taken you?'

She stiffened. 'It seemed to be what you imagined had happened,' she shrugged.

'Liar,' he said tautly. 'You wanted to hit back, didn't you, Leigh? Another little battle in our private war.'

'I hope some of the blows landed,' she said viciously.

His glance was mocking. 'Be careful, Leigh. Now who's making something personal out of our relationship? There's nothing as personal as a bitter wound, is there, Leigh?'

Her throat closed. Trembling, she met his eyes. 'Was it a bitter wound, Matt?'

He pushed her away to arm's length. 'If you don't want to be kissed to within an inch of your life you'd better get off home to Leicester now, woman,' he said thickly. 'Just remember in future, any provocative remarks from you can precipitate exactly the sort of incident you claim you wish to avoid.'

Leigh walked to the door, wishing her legs didn't tremble under her so violently. In the last few moments she had become so deeply aware of him that her whole system seemed to be disturbed to the point of anguished fever. For a moment she had felt she stood on the edge of an abyss, the flaw in her own cool character, from which Matt's touch could draw up blinding, consuming flame.

It had been Matt who drew back from the edge. She had forgotten her own condition for that moment. She had only been aware of the savage personal battle between them, and she knew that had he touched her at that moment he would have had an easy victory.

All the way back to Leicester she was eaten with self-contempt for how she had felt at that moment. She would not let him get to her again, she told herself. She would work with him as the perfect secretary, cool, self-contained, aloof. He would never be able to say she had provoked him into forgetting the condition she had laid down. Anything that happened would be his fault, and his alone, and she would see to it that he was punished for it in kind.

CHAPTER FIVE

SHE gave in her notice the following morning, feeling slightly guilty because she imagined it would cause both surprise and inconvenience, and was taken aback when her boss said, with a slight sigh, 'I guessed this would be coming.'

Leigh flushed to her hairline. 'What?'

The man shrugged. 'A lovely girl like you, Leigh, is going to find it hard to live with a broken engagement, but I'm not sure you're doing the right thing in running away ... I understand, all the same, and you have my blessing. I'm very sorry this has happened to someone as nice as you.'

Leigh shook, her eyes brightening with unshed tears. The kindness and thoughtfulness of the tone made her sense of guilt and her remorse far worse.

When she told her parents that she was leaving home for London and a new, much better job, her father shook out his newspaper and hid behind it, while her mother looked at her in distinct pity.

'Just as you like, dear,' she said.

Leaving the room, Leigh heard her murmur to her husband, 'She's taking it much harder than I'd thought she would.'

Wincing, Leigh went up to her bedroom and began to consider the practical problems of moving to London. She would have to find somewhere to live, she thought. That would be difficult. She knew all about the shortage of rented accommodation in the city.

She began to sort out her clothes, deciding which to take with her and which to leave behind. An hour later she heard her parents go out in the car. On Fridays they visited their closest friends to play bridge and gossip about the preceding week. She was sitting on her bed for the next half-hour, reading through old letters and school reports, grimacing over the great bundle of trivia she had found in a hatbox on top of her wardrobe. Why did one keep these things? She pushed them all back into the hatbox. They could all be thrown away. A piece of paper fell on to the floor and she picked it up, wincing as she read it. It was the first letter Phil had ever written to her, and she felt a wave of remorse and self-disgust as she pushed it into the hatbox.

It was unfair of life to offer such impossible choices, she thought. She might have been happy with Phil, but would Phil ever have been happy with her? Would it have been remotely fair to him to offer him affection when he needed passionate love? Life just didn't play fair with people.

A violent ring at the doorbell made her start. She went downstairs and opened the door, staring in shocked surprise at seeing Phil standing on the threshold, a bitter rage in his face.

He pushed past her, slamming the door, and she instinctively backed away from his taut, fury-stiffened figure.

'So you detest him, do you? You never want to see him again?' He spat the words out thickly. 'Then why the hell are you taking a job as his secretary, you lying little ...'

'Phil, don't,' she broke in shakily. 'Please!'

He shook her furiously. 'Why did you lie to me? You wanted to smooth me down, did you? It made it easier. Oh, God, have I been a blind fool where you're concerned! Secretary may be the word you've used to cover the job when you told your parents, but you and I know exactly what post you'll be filling, don't we? I imagine it's going to be very highly paid he's a wealthy man. Congratulations, Leigh.'

She almost slapped his face at the first biting insult, but behind his angry voice she heard the throb of a pain so deep her own heart winced at it, so she stood quietly, listening, letting him pour out his feelings, even though she was wounded by them.

For five minutes he tore her character to shreds, his face tight with bitterness, and she neither moved nor spoke, looking at him in regret.

At last he came to an abrupt stop, his voice choking. He turned, his back to her, and leaned against the wall. Leigh instinctively moved to touch his back, and he pushed her away with a rough hand.

'Don't touch me. Are you insane? If you come any closer I'll go completely out of my mind and do something we'll both regret.'

Leigh flushed, then, to her hairline.

He stood there for another moment, then straightened

and turned back to her. 'I'm not just saying this because I'm jealous,' he said stiffly. 'I am. You know just how jealous. But leaving that aside, Leigh, you can't do this. The sort of life he's offering you isn't your sort of world at all. He'll make you miserable one way or the other, and one day it will be over, and you'll have scars for the rest of your life.'

Softly, she said, 'Do you want my word of honour, Phil, that I'm taking a job as his secretary and nothing else?'

He held her blue gaze, and she saw a movement of doubt in his eyes.

'In fact,' she went on quietly, 'I only accepted the job on condition that he swore to keep it a business relationship only. It's a fascinating job, Phil. Highly paid, too. I've enjoyed working at my present job, but you must see how much more exciting it will be to work for the head of a newspaper organisation, instead of for some solicitor.'

Phil's eyes searched hers. He gave a low sigh. 'God knows why I should, but I believe you,' he said, grimacing. Then he shoved his hands into his pockets and leaned back against the wall, staring at her. 'All the same, if you think he offered you the job because of your brains and efficiency, you're out of your Chinese mind. The swine wants you, Leigh—I saw that from the beginning. When you danced with him at the hotel it was obvious that he fancied you, and then ...' He broke off, biting his lip. 'Anyway, you can't trust him, Leigh. He may have given you promises about keeping it all on the business level, but you can't trust him an inch.'

'I know that,' she said flatly.

'Then why?' he demanded, his eyes darkening jealously. 'Why?'

'I'm capable of looking after myself, Phil,' she said. 'I have no intention of becoming Mattieson Hume's mistress, now or in the future, so you'll just have to trust me to look after myself.'

'Do you think I can fly off to Saudi Arabia tomorrow leaving you at the tender mercies of that swine?' Phil demanded huskily. 'While I'm miles away who knows what could be happening to you? I'd go out of my mind wondering about it!'

'We're two separate people, Phil,' she reminded him gently. 'You mustn't worry about me. Don't even think about me. Enjoy your new life and forget me.'

'Forget you?' The cry came hoarsely. Phil looked at her with restless, glittering eyes, pulled her into his arms and sought her mouth hungrily. She resisted, turning her head away, and the resistance brought a sudden violence into the way he held her. She felt it surge into him, an inflamed, desperate emotion which alarmed her. He took her head between both hands, pushed it back and began to kiss her with utter savagery. She was unresponsive, shocked, dazed under it. She lost all count of time, beginning to feel almost faint, unable to breathe properly, her senses swirling, when he suddenly released her, his own breath harsh, stared at her out of passion-darkened eyes, and walked away out of the house, slamming the door behind him.

Leigh staggered upstairs and looked at herself in the bathroom mirror. Her lip was swollen and bruised and there were faint fingermarks already darkening on her pale throat. The marks of Phil's passion stood out like traces of guilt on her skin.

She began to cry helplessly, covering her face with her hands. She had deserved it, she had hurt him so badly. But shock left her dizzy and sick.

She did not dare to let her parents see these betraying marks. By the time they returned from their bridge evening she was in bed and pretending to be asleep. Her mother paused in the doorway, peering through the darkness towards her bed, then went out again, and Leigh turned over on to her face, fresh tears pouring down her cheeks.

In the morning those dark marks on mouth and throat were still clearly visible, and she dreaded having to explain them to her mother, but she got up late to find both her parents gone. Saturday was their busiest day at the antique shop and they always arrived early to prepare for the sudden rush of customers.

She was in the kitchen washing up her breakfast things, when someone knocked at the door.

Leigh's heart turned over. She stood for a moment, fighting a strong impulse of fear. Had Phil come back? She had dreaded seeing him again ever since yesterday. The moments when he kissed her were branded on her memory. She had been terribly conscious of the thin crust of civilisation which was all that kept him from breaking out of control altogether.

The knock came again, louder. She straightened her shoulders and went to the door, holding a wary, reserved expression on her face.

'You took long enough in answering the door,' said a familiar, mocking voice.

Her fear faded, her stiff body relaxed, as she saw Mattieson Hume leaning on the doorpost. 'Oh, it's you!'

He lifted a quizzical eyebrow. 'Who did you think it was?' Then his eyes narrowed on her and a harsh look came into his face.

He walked past her into the house. Leigh closed the door, and stood, head lowered, looking at the carpet.

'Why are you here?' she asked, having just realised the oddness of finding him on her doorstep on a Saturday morning.

'What happened, Leigh?' he asked abruptly, ignoring

her own question. 'It was him, I suppose. He's been here?' He lifted her chin and stared at her mouth, a grim twist to his lips.

'What are you doing here?' she repeated stubbornly. 'Are you forgetting my condition?'

'I'm like the elephant, I never forget,' he said drily. 'And if I have to beat you I'm going to get the story out of you, Leigh.'

She gave him a cold blue look. 'The story is perfectly obvious, isn't it?'

'Perfectly,' he said under his breath. 'The sooner I get you to London the better.'

'He's leaving himself tomorrow,' she told him.

'Why the hell did you see him?' he asked angrily. 'You're as incapable of reaching the obvious conclusions as a newborn child, Leigh. The man's crazy about you. You're playing with fire if you let him within touching distance.'

She half smiled. In a different context he was repeating the same warnings about Phil as Phil had given her about him. It was ironic.

He caught the stiff movement of her bruised mouth, and looked at her sharply. 'It isn't funny. He hurt you this time, didn't he, Leigh? You once told me he wasn't capable of hurting anyone, but you were wrong, weren't you? Given enough provocation any man can be savage.'

'I don't blame Phil,' she said.

'Don't blame him?' His face darkened.

'I deserved it,' she said wearily. 'I hurt him, and I feel as guilty as hell about it. He was out of control, just for a moment, and I've no doubt he regrets it now.'

Matt Hume looked at her as if working out what to say next. 'Get your coat, Leigh,' he said after a pause. 'I'm taking you out to lunch.'

'No, thank you,' she said stiffly. 'I'm not going out.'

'We have to discuss the practical details of your move to London,' he said patiently. 'You'll need somewhere to live, and I have an idea of somewhere that would suit you.'

'Why, you . . .' Her voice broke in sudden rage. 'If you think I'd let you set me up in a flat. . . !'

He put a hand over her mouth, grinning in amusement. 'Oh, what a wicked mind you have, Leigh! Now stop glaring at me and listen. Our porter, Sam, has a large, rather rambling Victorian house in Islington. His twin sons got married a month ago and moved out, so he and his wife have more space than they know what to do with. Sam thought of turning the top floor of the house into a flat, and when he mentioned it to me, I thought of you. He's agreed to let you have first refusal.'

She stared at him over his silencing hand, her eyes expressive. He took his hand away. His eyes teased her. 'Well?'

'That sounds marvellous,' she admitted, a little grudgingly.

'You sound disappointed,' he mocked. 'Hoped I was suggesting I set you up in a flat with all the luxuries of life, Leigh?'

She moved to slap him and he caught her wrist. Their eyes held in silence.

'That's about the third time you've tried to hit me,' he said softly. 'If you weren't already very bruised I'd slap you hard, Leigh. Now, take warning. Control that temper of yours.'

'I haven't got a temper,' she said, jerking on her wrist to free herself.

He raised an eyebrow. 'Are you kidding?'

'I didn't have one until I met you,' she said sulkily.

He gave her a suddenly charming, coaxing smile. 'That's the nicest thing you've ever said to me, darling.'

Leigh's heart missed a beat. She felt hot colour run up her face as she realised the hidden implications of her admission that he affected her so deeply.

To cover herself, she snapped, 'Don't call me darling!'

His eyes caressed her. 'Don't you like it, Leigh?'

Her heart was beating so fast it sounded like a drum in her own ears. She swallowed, moving away. 'Thank you for finding me a flat, Mr Hume, but I still can't come out to lunch with you.' She gave a faint laugh. 'I'd feel rather too conspicuous. People would be bound to stare at these marks.'

'Yes,' he said consideringly, 'I'd forgotten that.' He stood, watching her. 'It's a lovely day, Leigh, the perfect day for a picnic. Why don't I go and find some picnic food and come back and drive you somewhere peaceful?'

'No,' she said raggedly. 'I told you, I won't go out with you.'

'Not when I've driven all this way?' he asked plaintively.

'No!'

'Then we'll stay here,' he said in a satisfied tone.

She looked at him, infuriated. 'You're doing nothing of the sort. Mr Hume, will you please go?'

'Matt,' he said, moving into the kitchen. 'If you like, I'll make the coffee.'

She followed him into the room, her shoulders tense, to find him already moving about in easy familiarity, finding the coffee and the percolator, setting out cups. She watched him, almost speechless at her inability to move him from his intended course.

'Is this how you're going to keep our agreement?' she asked his lean back as he worked. 'I might have known I couldn't trust you for a moment.'

'Leigh,' he said, in sudden soberness, turning to face her, 'I promised you I wouldn't attempt to seduce you, and I never break my word. I never intended to accept our relationship as a purely business one. We're going to spend a great deal of time together in the future, and if you imagine that two people thrown together for hour after hour, day after day, can remain purely business acquaintances, you're wildly wrong. You've got to start to think of me as a colleague. Stop calling me Mr Hume. Stop treating me as if I were a leper. We can be friends, can't we?'

She met the straight, frank look of the grey eyes and was thrown into confusion. Put like that, she was behaving very stupidly.

'Miss Harrison didn't call you Matt,' she said lamely.

He laughed, his eyes dancing. 'Of course she didn't —not in front of you. Barbara is discreet, a perfect secretary. When we're alone she uses christian names. So do I. But in front of anyone else she reverts to my surname. It can give a wrong impression if we seem to be too familiar. Gossip spreads very fast in a big organisation— you should know that. The fact that Barbara and I are just friends would never be an exciting titbit of gossip, but if people could imagine we were more they'd build it up into a great romance.' He grimaced. 'You've no idea how people love to embroider. It would be useless to tell them that Barbara adores her future husband and regards me as just her boss. They would rather believe a more racy version.'

Leigh sat down on a kitchen stool, her long slender legs crossed, and watched as he deftly made the coffee and found cream in the refrigerator. 'I liked Barbara,' she said quietly. She believed him when he said that there was nothing between himself and his secretary. Barbara's eyes were too clear, too warm, for him to be lying.

He turned his dark head and grinned at her. 'She's a very nice girl,' he agreed. 'Efficient, too. I shall miss her.'

Her smile was teasing. 'Meaning you suspect I'm neither?'

He gave her an amused look. 'Don't fish, Leigh. I'm sure you're very efficient.'

A slight dimple dented her mouth. 'But not very nice?'

He didn't answer, and she looked up to find his grey eyes narrowed in speculation on her. 'You find it as impossible as I do, don't you, Leigh?' he asked softly at her look.

'To do what?' she asked in bewilderment.

'Keep things impersonal between us,' he said mockingly.

Her colour rose and she looked down. Why on earth had she slid into flirting with him like that? she asked herself angrily. She could hardly blame him this time. She knew she was the one who had opened the perfectly direct conversation into a distinctly personal exchange.

They sat down and drank their coffee in a peculiarly conscious silence. Leigh was wondering how on earth she was going to force him to leave, when he said softly, 'What shall we have for lunch?'

'You can't stay,' she said flatly. 'No, Matt.'

He grinned at her. 'I'll cook it. Omelette?'

'No,' she said desperately.

His eyes teased her. 'You look quite petrified, Leigh. All I offered was an omelette.'

For a moment her inclination to be with him warred with her knowledge of the dangers of being alone in this house with him. She stared at the table, her finger tracing an endless circle.

'Cheese?' he suggested. 'I noticed all the ingredients when I was making the coffee.'

'Is there anything you can't do?' she asked him in despair. 'You're totally maddening, do you know that?'

'I've been told before,' he agreed. 'Is cheese all right with you?'

She looked at him, her face torn between warring instincts. 'I suppose if I asked you to go right now you'd take no notice?'

His mouth twitched. 'Precisely,' he said mockingly. 'So don't waste your time, Leigh.'

'If I were a man I'd throw you out bodily,' she snapped furiously.

'If you were a man I wouldn't need to be asked twice,' he said in amused reply.

'What on earth am I supposed to tell my parents when they come back?' she demanded. 'How do I explain your presence?'

He grinned. 'I've come to explain certain details of the job to you, Leigh. In fact, before lunch, that's exactly what I will do.' He pulled out a piece of paper from his jacket, spreading it out on the table between them. 'I've made a list of necessary items you must know about. When you start work I won't be there for the first three days—I'm going to New York. But there are some aspects of the job I want to emphasise personally. Barbara will no doubt fill you in on them, but I want to be sure you understand the delicacy of the position myself.'

She nodded. 'I see.'

He began to talk, his face serious, and she saw a new side of him, a crisp, hard, clear-headed mind emerging behind the casual façade of his charm.

'I've no doubt you're aware of the problems facing Fleet Street with regard to the New Technology ... basically, we're in the process of changing from an old-established craft industry dominated by the print unions because of the enormous strength of their necessary skills to a new, wide open situation brought about by the invention of computerised printing. At the moment this is largely in the land of wishful thinking because, obviously, the unions are dragging their feet over it, and the last thing we want is a prolonged strike. The situation is delicately balanced at the moment. You have to know the background, Leigh, and understand the problems in detail.'

He began to explain the process of computerised technology to her, his mind quick and clear, and she listened with a great interest, realising more clearly than ever how clever and shrewd a man Matt was beneath his sophisticated exterior.

'It's not so much a matter of progress or increased efficiency and profit,' he sighed. 'It's at the moment a matter of management relations. Before we can install the new machinery we have to convince the unions it's necessary. Printing is incredibly costly. Our costs go up year by year and our profits aren't keeping in line with them. Sooner or later we'll reach breaking point. We can't afford to run the papers without making a profit, and if we close down, all those jobs go for good. So on both sides some sort of arrangement will become essential. In the meantime we're all walking a tightrope.' He looked at her soberly. 'As my secretary, you have to be aware of the need for extreme caution and care when dealing with the unions.'

'I understand,' she nodded.

Matt's eyes searched hers. He gave her a brief, approving smile. 'Yes, I'm sure you can manage,' he said.

Leigh glanced at the kitchen clock, amazed to realise that they had been talking about the new technology for an hour. 'Good heavens, look at the time!' she gasped.

He grinned. 'Hungry?'

'Starving,' she said.

He got up. 'You grate the cheese, I'll beat up the eggs.

Shall we have salad with the omelette? I saw some in the fridge.'

'I'll make some dressing when I've grated the cheese,' she offered.

'Fine,' he said, reaching into a cupboard for a large bowl. Leigh watched for a second or two, amused by his deft efficiency as he began to break eggs, then set to work herself.

They ate in the kitchen. She was surprised and impressed by the golden, beautifully creamy omelette he had made, and congratulated him on it.

'I have a limited repertoire,' he said casually, 'but what I do I do well.'

She laughed. 'Modesty isn't your strong point, is it?'

He flickered an amused look at her. 'Is it yours, Leigh?'

Her eyes widened. 'I'd never considered it. Maybe not. Phil says I'm spoilt. Too much admiration, too much consideration from my parents . . . I've had life too easy so far.'

Matt's eyes moved over her unreadably. 'What were you like at school, Leigh?'

'Much as I am today,' she said. 'I grew up early. My parents treated me as an adult long before I'd got out of adolescence, so I matured early.'

He looked down at his long, capable hands. 'What about boys? Many boy-friends before Phil came along?'

She laughed. 'Dozens, but none of them mattered.'

His head came up and he stared at her, eyes narrowed. 'And he did?'

She flushed slightly. 'He was more serious than the others,' she said defiantly. 'He went on seeing me.'

'You mean you shook the others off without a problem,' he translated thoughtfully. 'You learnt how to give a brush-off early in life, I suspect, Leigh. With your looks you would have had to.'

She shrugged, embarrassed. 'Shall we wash up?'

'Don't change the subject,' he said calmly. 'Leigh, was there never anyone?'

Her skin grew hot and her eyes flickered nervously. 'I don't want to discuss my private life,' she said. 'I would rather get on with the washing up.'

As she got up his hand clamped down on to her wrist, holding her. 'What was he like?' he asked softly.

Her blue eyes widened. She looked at him, taken aback. After a moment she asked shakily, 'Who?'

'The one who hurt you so that you'd never let another man get close enough to do it again,' he said.

Leigh caught her breath. She looked at him with bitterness. 'You're so damned shrewd, Matt, aren't you? Give you a problem and you worry at it until you've worked it out.'

'It wasn't difficult,' he said drily. 'You just might have been a cold woman, but that possibility soon went out of the window.'

Her eyes burned at him furiously. 'Shut up!'

He ignored her rage. 'So there had to be another reason for the glacial manner, the determination to be in control of the situation between yourself and any man who came near you. From that point it was simple. The answer was obvious. At some time in your life a man had hurt you, and you'd wrapped yourself in ice to prevent it happening again.'

'Well, if that's settled to your satisfaction, maybe you'd like to be on your way back to London,' Leigh said sharply.

'We were going to do the washing up,' Matt said in bland tones. He got up and began to clear the table.

Leigh fumed, eyeing him with a deep desire to smash one of the plates over his dark head.

'Are you going to help me or are you just going to stand there smoking like Mount Vesuvius, Leigh?' he asked mockingly.

She snatched up a tea towel and went to join him at the sink. They worked in silence for a while, then Matt said conversationally, 'So what sort of chap was he?'

'Shut up,' Leigh said tightly.

'Good-looking,' Matt mused. 'Older than you, I guess. A flirt.'

Leigh's temper shot sky high. Bitterly, she said, 'He was like you ... a good-looking, deceitful, conceited swine, and married to boot.'

He lifted an eyebrow, his face sharp. 'Did you know he was married?'

'Not when I met him,' she said tightly. 'When I found out it was finished.'

'Ah,' he said on a low sound of satisfaction. 'So that's it.'

'Yes,' she said, her voice shaking with anger, 'that's it.'

Matt dried his hands, having finished washing up, and leaned on the table, watching as she put the china away.

'How long ago was it?' he asked.

She turned on him. 'I don't want to talk about it.'

He caught her by her elbows and shook her slightly. 'You know I'm going to find out, Leigh. Tell me now and get it over with. How long ago?'

'I was seventeen,' she said, her voice full of remembered bitter feeling. 'I was infatuated with him and if I hadn't found out about his wife I would have slept with him ... there, is that enough, Matt? Or do you want to hear every single detail?'

He put a hand to her face, his fingers curving over her hot, flushed cheek, their tips caressing. 'Seventeen,' he said flatly. 'You poor kid. It was a brutal beginning, Leigh, but you've got to let it fade into the past for your own sake.'

'I've never thought of him again,' she said savagely.

His eyes looked down into her wide, angry blue ones. 'You've thought of nothing else for years, have you, Leigh?' he asked softly. 'Oh, I'm not saying you're still in love with him, but he hurt your pride and your self-respect deeply, and you're still trying to build a permanent wall around yourself so that it can never happen again.'

'So clever, Matt,' she said in angry mockery.

'By turning yourself into a frozen statue, you're letting him go on hurting you, Leigh,' he said seriously. 'If you could have shrugged off what happened he would have faded completely by now, but you've built your whole life from what he did to you, so the effect of the bastard has lasted ever since.'

It was true, Leigh thought in sudden realisation. She looked at him curiously, realising that he was the first person she had ever told about what happened. It irritated her that he should have winkled the admission out of her. He was too shrewd, too experienced, too quick.

'I think you'd better go,' she said huskily, suddenly aware of the erotic movements of his hands as they shaped and caressed her face between their palms.

He was looking at her lazily, his grey eyes unreadable. 'Yes,' he said, surprising her, 'I must go in a minute. I have a dinner date tonight.'

'With Cathy Lord?' she asked, a jealous qualm shooting through her.

His eyes narrowed. A smile curved his mouth. 'With Cathy,' he agreed blandly. 'Pretty, isn't she?'

'Very,' Leigh agreed, moving backward to free herself.

His hands were immovable, holding her head warmly. 'Let me go, Matt,' she said huskily.

His eyes were on her mouth. She felt a quiver run over it and tried to hold it stiffly.

Suddenly Matt smiled at her, his charm powerful. 'Every human being has two citadels, Leigh one in the body, the other in the heart. If you're honest, you know that in our private war it would be simple for me to conquer one of your citadels. It's without defence, isn't it, Leigh? My weapons are too powerful for you.'

She stared at him without answering, suddenly tense.

'We're going to be working closely together from next week,' he went on conversationally. 'I don't want you worrying permanently in case I suddenly attack that undefended citadel of yours, Leigh. I give you my word of honour I've no intention of taking it by surprise.'

She was breathing erratically, her eyes fixed on his face.

He grinned. 'I must go. I'll see you next weekend. I'll come down on the Saturday and drive you to Sam's house. Expect me at around eleven, and be ready. My plane for New York leaves on Sunday at an absurdly early hour, so I want to get an early night on Saturday.'

He walked down the hall and Leigh watched as he went out of the front door. He gave her a last, brief look from the grey eyes, then he was gone.

CHAPTER SIX

THE following Saturday Leigh was packed and ready to leave when Matt came to the front door at exactly ten-thirty. She had already said goodbye to her parents, who had left for their shop, and was feeling extremely nervous as she opened the door to him. There were going to be enormous changes in her life after today. From living in a familiar street, a town she knew well, among friends and relations, she would be living in a great city which was comparatively unknown to her, and working in an exciting, vast new industry, learning every day and stretched to her full capacity to cope with her work.

Matt's cold grey eyes had a smile at the back of them as he took her cases from her hands. 'Ready, Leigh?' he asked softly, and a great deal of unspoken curiosity lay behind the phrase.

She lifted her chin. 'Yes, thank you.'

He grinned. 'No need to gird on your armour. The battle hasn't begun yet!'

In the car she looked at him sideways, obliquely observing him through her long lashes. He drove as expertly as he did everything else, a hard assurance in the way he wove in and out of the traffic, alert to coming problems and already taking action to avoid trouble before it arrived. The hard, clear profile was instinct with power. Intelligence, experience, confidence marked him as a man to be viewed with respect and, if you were a woman, slight apprehension.

'Did you see your ex-fiancé before he left the country?' he asked suddenly, shooting into a clear patch of road with a rapid acceleration which left slower cars behind.

'No,' she said.

'He must have felt whatever happened between you was final,' he murmured.

She made no reply.

He glanced at her. 'Were the bruises on your face and throat the only ones he gave you, Leigh?'

The shrewdness of the question brought a flush. 'He said a great deal,' she admitted.

'Getting his own back,' Matt commented.

'No, he was bitter because he'd heard I was going to work for you,' she said defiantly.

Matt grimaced. 'And his view of what sort of position you'd be occupying?'

'You can guess that without having to be told,' she said flatly.

'You disabused him of the idea?'

Her voice stiffened. 'Naturally.'

'Naturally,' he said with amusement.

'It wasn't funny,' she snapped.

'No, poor devil,' Matt muttered.

'Stop talking about him,' she said angrily. 'It's over. I want to forget it.'

He glanced at her oddly. 'You never loved him at all, did you, Leigh?'

'I was fond of him,' she said, her mouth firm. 'I still am. He's a very nice man. I wish I was in love with him. If I could have been, I would have been ...'

His brows drew together. 'You tried to make yourself fall in love and couldn't, Leigh?'

She sighed. 'I suppose so.'

He drove in silence for a long time, his eyes on the road, his face shuttered and impossible to read. Quietly, some half-hour later, he asked her. 'Were you completely crazy over that chap when you were seventeen, Leigh?'

Her heart seemed to squeeze in agony. She stared at the road ahead. In harsh self-mockery, she said, 'Completely.'

Matt said nothing, but the speed of the car shot up and they swished past the other traffic on the motorway at ninety miles an hour.

'You're going too fast,' she told him in alarm.

He gradually eased off without speaking. Leigh looked curiously at his hard, dark face. She was beginning to know him. He was angry about something. She suspected that he was capable of enormous compassion despite the tough exterior. He was sorry for Phil, oddly sympathetic to him, despite his faint contempt for him. Was he sorry for her, too? Had her admission that she had been so wildly in love at seventeen and been so badly hurt angered him on her behalf?

He was a strange man, she thought. There was that trace of cruelty in his mouth and eyes, yet a gentleness there too. She had been shown both.

They stopped at one o'clock at a small country hotel a few miles outside the beginning of the London suburbs to eat lunch. Matt made a charming companion throughout the meal, his manner quietly teasing at times, attentive, amusing, friendly.

They drew a certain amount of attention among the other guests. Catching a glimpse of their table in a long wall mirror Leigh saw Matt's handsome, dark head inclined towards her, his well-cut expensive clothes and assured manner underlining his good looks, while she was taken aback by an unexpected softness in her own face, her blue eyes caught smiling back at him as he talked, her smooth blonde head tilted in amusement. Anyone looking at them might be excused for imagining an extremely personal relationship, she admitted, with something of a shock. The realisation of how far he had got under her skin froze her.

Matt considered the change in her expression with lifted brows. 'Something wrong?'

'No,' she said stiffly.

He looked at her shrewdly. Calling for the bill, he leaned back, staring at her, and she could sense that quick brain trying to work out what had caused the change in her.

They drove into London in comparative silence. Leigh was cool and offhand, determined not to succumb again to the charm of his quick smile. Every time he looked at her in that way she felt the pull of an attraction so strong her struggles against it were physically draining.

Islington, she discovered, was an enormous sprawling London district which had long streets of beautifully proportioned early Victorian houses in it; their flat windows, shallow steps and stuccoed façades were elegant even when they had been neglected for years and left to moulder and decay. Many of them, however, had been carefully preserved, and she was delighted to discover that Sam's house was one which had been lovingly restored to something approaching its original beauty.

Standing on the pavement beside Matt she looked up in admiration. The house was one of a long terrace. It had three storeys, above ground, and a barred-window basement below ground. It had been freshly painted in white and pale blue. A bright window box enlivened the windows on the ground floor, the reds, yellows and purples of petunias blazing against the white woodwork.

'The top floor will be your home from now on,' Matt told her, watching her appreciative face.

She turned a smile on him, her blue eyes bright. 'It's fantastic, Matt! I love it.'

He smiled, taking her arm. 'That's the first time I've ever seen real warmth in your smile, do you know that?' he asked lazily. 'Come and have a chat with Mrs Sam.'

Mrs Sam turned out to be a very small, bird-like woman with silvery grey hair, bright eyes and a ready smile. She told them that Sam had just popped out. 'Gone to the betting shop,' she grinned at Matt.

'Backing Printer's Devil in the three-thirty, is he?' Matt asked, his grey eyes dancing.

Mrs Sam laughed. 'You know Sam, he always bets on impulse. Did you back it, Matt?'

Leigh was astonished to hear her use his christian name, and her quick look of surprise caught his grey eyes. A gleam of mockery came into his look back.

'No,' he said lightly. 'I backed on form, as I always do. I believe in form, not impulse.'

'Ah, well,' said Mrs Sam. 'It takes all sorts.'

'The bookies must make a lot out of Sam,' Matt said drily.

'He enjoys it,' said Mrs Sam, slightly defensive.

'That's all that matters,' Leigh said to back her up.

Matt turned a mocking eye on her. 'Is that really what you think?' he asked under his breath as they followed Mrs Sam up the narrow stairs.

Leigh ignored him.

Mrs Sam paused on the landing. 'I'm afraid there are a lot of stairs,' she said apologetically.

'Leigh's young,' said Matt. 'She can manage them.' His glance slid over her slender figure, lingering on her long legs. 'And she has very strong ankles.'

Mrs Sam laughed. She gave Leigh a wink. 'Here you are, dear.' She pointed proudly to a freshly painted white door. 'Your own front door.' Unlocking it, she turned to hand Leigh the keys. 'You'll want to be private,' she said. 'It's completely self-contained.'

Leigh walked into the flat, feeling odd. For the first time in her life she would be living alone. She had always lived at home until now, and the prospect was both exciting and alarming.

The flat was delightful. It had been furnished with clean, modern furniture which was attractive without being strong in character. The ceilings were high, the windows tall. Light streamed into the rooms. Mrs Sam followed her, explaining about the various rooms.

'You see, you've got your sitting-room, your bedroom and your kitchen,' she said, a satisfied look on her face. 'The kitchen was a bedroom. It's a bit small, but it's got everything you'll need.' She opened a door. 'This is the bathroom . . . newly installed. Nice, isn't it?'

'It's simply lovely,' Leigh said enthusiastically. 'I never expected to find anywhere as nice as this.' She looked at the other woman gratefully. 'Thank you very much.'

Mrs Sam beamed. 'We're glad to have a good tenant who comes with high references,' she said, her eyes moving to Matt. 'If Matt trusts you we know we can.'

Leigh glanced at him and found that disturbing, teasing smile on his handsome face.

'Well,' said Mrs Sam, 'sorry to rush off, but I've got a cake in the oven and I must get off to see it comes out on time. If you'd like to come down in half an hour, both of you, I'll give you some tea.'

'Thank you,' said Matt cheerfully, before Leigh could reply. 'We'd love to.'

When she had gone an odd silence fell between the two left in the flat. Leigh wandered around, admiring things, feeling like a child given a beautiful dolls house to play with, and half wishing Matt would go instead of standing there, watching her.

'Now, Leigh,' he said as she ran out of things to look at,

'tell me what went wrong over lunch?'

She frowned. 'What do you mean?'

His mouth was quizzical. 'You were completely at ease one minute, the next I was looking at a woman with ice-cold eyes. What went on inside that complicated little mind of yours?'

'Nothing,' she shrugged. 'Shall we go down to have our tea now?'

He caught her hand as she moved to pass him and the touch sent a wild flutter along her pulses. She looked at him, off balance, her eyes darkening.

Matt made a sound under his breath, and pulled her towards him. Unable to resist, she curved into his arms, her mouth raised, and they kissed, their mouths exploring each other in slow, warm sensuality, her arms round his neck, a sensation of drugged bliss encapsulating her from all thought.

When they drew apart Leigh felt she had been poised on the brink of a momentous discovery and had come back too soon from the golden Eden into which he had taken her, so that she looked from his dark face to the room in which they stood with bewilderment. While they were in each other's arms time seemed to have stopped. The clocks had frozen in crystal silence. The golden sunlight had not moved. Now time flowed on relentlessly. The wind in a plane tree outside sent a flickering shadow pattern running across the floor. The clocks had begun to tick again. Leigh's heartbeat was loudly audible to her.

Matt was looking down at her oddly, his dark face unreadable, yet a curious expression which she could not decipher in his grey eyes. She looked back at him, knowing that in the last few moments they had torn up the agreement on which she had based her acceptance of a job with him, yet unable to voice any protest, because she knew very well that she had invited it. She had wanted to be in his arms so badly at that instant that her eyes had openly told him so, and, being the man he was, he had responded.

'No comeback, Leigh?' he asked drily.

She lowered her head, her flush growing. 'We'd better go and have that tea,' she said huskily.

Without a word he turned and left the flat and she followed him, so shaken by what had happened that she felt weak. Remembering what he had said to her about her undefended citadel, she knew that had he decided to use all his power against her at that moment she would have fallen to him without so much as a token struggle. Yet he had withdrawn his forces, although she sensed that he, too, had known that her defences were completely down.

Sam had just come in when they got downstairs. In the large, cosy kitchen they all sat down to drink tea and eat slices of warm, rich fruit cake, while Sam and Matt argued about racing, and Leigh listened to them with amusement, seeing a side of Matt she had never seen before. It was clear that his relationship with Sam and his wife was an old one, based on mutual liking and trust.

Mrs Sam asked Leigh about her previous job, and was interested in hearing about her home in Leicester, the family antique shop and her family. 'I've got something you'd like to see,' she said, getting up and opening a cupboard. She thrust a small porcelain figure into Leigh's hands. 'There, do you like that?'

Leigh gently turned it around in her smooth white hands. 'It's lovely,' she said warmly. 'Meissen ... have you got the pair? Or just this one?'

Sam chuckled. 'Just the one, Leigh,' he nodded. 'Mind you, she's been looking for the one that matches it for years. Her mother left it to her twenty years ago. Dotes on that thing, she does.'

Leigh smiled at Mrs Sam. 'I don't blame you,' she agreed. 'It's beautiful.' Her eyes returned to the figure. She could feel the delicacy of the glaze under her fingertips. 'If the pair ever comes into my family shop I'll ask them to keep it for you,' she said. 'They'd be worth quite a bit if you had them both. Apart, they're worth far less.'

Mrs Sam looked pleased. She received the figure back tenderly and replaced it in the glass-fronted china cupboard.

Matt stood up. 'I must go,' he said regretfully. 'I have a lot to do before I catch that plane tomorrow.' He smiled at Sam and his wife. 'I'll be seeing you, then.'

'Be careful in New York, Matt,' Sam said in fatherly concern. 'A very violent place, they say.'

'I'll be careful,' said Matt, his grin easy.

Leigh had stood up, hesitating. He glanced at her, his eyes coolly shuttered. 'Walk with me to the door, Leigh,' he said lightly. 'I've a few last-minute instructions to give you.'

She followed him out to his car and he leaned on the smooth top of it, his hand raking back his thick silver-flecked black hair as he surveyed her.

'If anything bothers you while I'm away you can trust Sam to the hilt,' he said. 'He'll he glad to help you. Are you all right for money, Leigh? London's more expensive than Leicester. If you need a loan until your first month's salary arrives I could see to that easily.'

'No, thank you,' she said. 'I've got quite a fair amount of savings.'

He nodded. 'Sure?'

'Quite sure,' she said flatly.

There was a breath of summer wind blowing through the plane tree, sending that flickering diamond pattern over her calm face, giving a shifting brightness to her hair.

Matt's eyes studied her coolly. 'I'll see you when I get back, then,' he said after a moment.

Leigh nodded. 'Have a nice trip.'

He walked round to the driver's door and unlocked it. Leigh watched him get inside. The engine roared into life, he gave her a brief look, a wave and was gone.

She felt cold as she walked back in the new flat, confronting the beginning of her new life with a chill of loneliness.

Sam knocked on her door an hour later, asking if she needed any help in settling in, and offering advice on the best shops in the neighbourhood. Leigh and he walked down the stairs together talking and then she walked round to do some shopping for the weekend, buying all the provisions she thought she would need. On her return, Mrs Sam asked if she wanted to place a daily order for milk. 'I can see to it when he comes tomorrow,' she offered. Leigh ordered one pint a day and stopped to chat for ten minutes, already beginning to feel that she was at home with the older woman.

'Sam could give you a lift to work each day,' Mrs Sam offered. 'He starts at eight-thirty, so it would be a bit early for you, but it would save you the bus fare. No need to accept if you prefer to make your own way, but he'd like the company, if you don't mind getting up earlier.'

'I'd be very grateful,' said Leigh, taken by surprise. 'If he's sure it would be no trouble.'

'Sam would enjoy having an ear to bend,' Mrs Sam laughed, her eyes twinkling. 'It seems silly both of you going to the same place and not going together.'

Leigh went to bed that night feeling a little lost, a little lonely, yet not unhappy. That Sunday she spent the whole day touring London at her leisure, taking buses from place to place, eating her meals out when it occurred to her. When she got back to the flat she was worn out and aching from head to foot. Mrs Sam heard her come in and came out to speak to her.

'Had a good day?' Her kind eyes saw the weariness in Leigh's face. 'What you need is a cup of tea. I've got a pot made.'

'Oh, Mrs Sam, I'm dying for tea,' Leigh admitted with a groan, following her into the kitchen.

She sat in a chair, nursing her aching body, drinking hot tea and listening to Mrs Sam talking about her twin sons, Andrew and George. 'Like as two peas in a pod to look at, and yet they're so different in character. Andy, he's the practical one, very level-headed and shrewd. But Georgie! Daft as a brush even now, but he's got such a warm heart nobody could hold anything against him.' She moved on to dissect her daughters-in-law, kindly yet shrewdly. 'Andy's wife is a nice, sensible girl and they'll be very happy together, but my Georgie got a peach of a girl ... Diana, pretty, loving, a real daughter to me already. I've nothing against Andy's wife, Sue, but I can tell right now that she and I are chalk and cheese.'

Leigh found it soothing to sit and listen to the family stories from the past, the little bits of local gossip, the comments on the neighbourhood shops. When Mrs Sam began to talk about Matt, though, her heart leapt, as though even his name had power over her.

'Always more of a family friend than a boss he's been to me and Sam. Mind, we've known him for years now. It started when the twins were little. My Georgie had meningitis—nearly died, he did. Matt heard he was ill and he sent me some flowers and he insisted on paying for the best possible treatment for Georgie. He came round here to see how he was and stayed for tea. The next week he came round with a train set for the boys. He took to Georgie somehow. Used to visit us often, bringing him and Andy little presents.'

'That was very kind of him,' Leigh said, trying to reconcile this picture of Matt with the image of the cold, shrewd intelligent man she had first seen across the dining-room of a London hotel, the power of his physical presence imprinted with his worldly authority.

Mrs Sam smiled. 'He is kind,' her voice said softly. 'You know that, Leigh. Of course, he was younger then, softer. He must have been nothing but a boy himself.'

Leigh half smiled at the idea of Matt as a boy, and Mrs Sam caught the look and chuckled.

'He was,' she insisted. 'In his early twenties, just beginning to take the reins at World Gazette. His father, Mr Stephen, he was Chairman in those days. Matt got the job pushed on to him early when Mr Stephen had a heart attack. Of course, he didn't die, but he had to take things easy, and Matt took to it like a duck to water. I think he came round here to get away from all that. Responsibility is a terrible burden, Leigh, and Matt's responsible for every living soul at World Gazette. He never forgets it. Oh, he can be tough and lay down the law when he has to, but he's like my Georgie, he's a man of very deep feelings, even though he doesn't let them show on the surface. Georgie, now, he shows everything. He's never learnt to be like Matt and hide how he feels, but then in Matt's world I suppose you have to learn to hide things or you get eaten alive.'

'Yes,' said Leigh absently, her heart racing as she thought about him. It had never occurred to her that he might have deep feelings. She had seen him more as a brain embedded in a very sexy, attractive body. The combination of sexual promise with cold intelligence had been oddly chilling.

In her flat later she sat listening to a cassette of Bach's Violin Concerto, her mind more on Matt than on the music, even though Menuhin's playing wound itself delicately into her ear and tugged at her attention.

Could she be wrong about Mattieson Hume? Mrs Sam's view of him was so opposed to her own. She had seen him as a hard-headed, egotistical man who had made cold plans to marry Cathy Lord because she was a suitable wife, while intending to carry on with his casual seductions afterwards. Now she wondered if he were possibly in love with Cathy.

She bit her lip, her teeth worrying the soft skin irritably. It would be easy enough for him to fall in love with Cathy Lord. She was very pretty, very presentable, a girl from his own world who would understand exactly how to adapt to fit his life style.

Unable to sit still, she moved around the flat, frowning, touching books, a vase, a pile of cassettes, her hands cold.

She didn't give a damn whether Matt loved Cathy Lord or not, she told herself impatiently. The only feelings she had towards him were ones of angry self-contempt because of the effect he had on her senses. He had none at all on her emotions. She despised herself because she felt that violent pull of attraction. It was purely a chemical reaction, she reminded herself. She didn't feel anything more.

She stood in front of a mirror, staring at her own reflection. She was wearing a soft blue silk blouse and a pair of white jeans which clung to her body like a second skin, giving her a slender outline which curved softly from waist to knee. Her silken hair was loose because she had washed it. It glittered in the lamplight, the fine strands like threads of white-gold silk against her skin. A warm colour rose in her face as she remembered the moments yesterday when she had been in Matt's arms, the mundane world abandoned, responsive only to his mouth.

Could a man who was in love with another girl make love like that?

Her eyes frowned and she moved away irritably. Matt puzzled and annoyed her. She didn't understand him. The contradictory puzzle of his mind was locked against her. He had seemed so simple at first, but now Mrs Sam had disturbed her view of him. She did not know what to make of him. She only knew that she could not get him out of her mind, and that that fact disturbed her deeply.

Next morning Sam drove her to the great plate-glass edifice of World Gazette and dropped her outside while he drove on into the car park beneath the building.

Leigh went into the lobby and was greeted at once by a security man, who glanced at her pass, given to her by Sam that morning as an afterthought. 'Have to be hot on security, Leigh,' he explained. 'You get a lot of nuts wandering in off the street otherwise—not to mention criminals and terrorists. Now, don't lose that pass or you'll have a lot of trouble getting into the building.'

Leigh went up in the lift and found Matt's offices empty. She began to wander around, learning the feel of the place, quite enjoying the sensation of being alone there for a while. Barbara arrived at nine-fifteen, flushed and excited.

She grinned at Leigh. 'Oh, lord, you're early and I'm late. I'm sorry, I missed my bus.'

'It doesn't matter,' Leigh said pleasantly. 'I had to get here early as I shall be getting a lift to work by car and that's the only time I can arrive.'

'Lucky you,' said Barbara enviously. 'Found somewhere to live?'

'Yes,' said Leigh, not mentioning that it was with Sam. She sensed it might be best to be discreet about that. It might cause comment, and she preferred to find her own way around before arousing talk.

The telephone rang and Barbara made a face. 'Here

we go,' she said. 'Once it starts it never stops!'

The day went past rapidly. At lunchtime Barbara took Leigh to the office canteen, a long white-tiled room crammed with people, the noise rising in waves until it bounced off the ceiling.

'Like feeding time at the Zoo,' Barbara commented drily.

The food was inexpensive and edible, although it mainly seemed to consist of things with chips. Leigh chose one of the three salads displayed in a cold cupboard. Barbara, eating the day's special of shepherd's pie, gave her a wry grin.

'I ought to eat salad, but I'm starving,' she said. Her eyes ran over Leigh's slender, elegant figure in the cream suit she was wearing. 'Did you say there was a man in your life? Because if there isn't you'll soon be snowed under with offers, judging by the looks you're getting from the reporters over there!'

Involuntarily Leigh glanced in the direction Barbara had indicated and met several pairs of curious, admiring eyes. She glanced away again without expression and looked back at Barbara.

'Do I gather that the various departments tend to sit together?' she asked.

Barbara laughed. 'More or less. They sit with friends, of course, and that usually means whoever they work with. The printers tend to rush off to the nearest pub. It's very hot down in the printing works and they're dying for a drink by the time they knock off for lunch, or supper. Some of the older ones drink in here with a meal, but usually the young ones go to the pub.'

Leigh nodded. Barbara's eyes lifted with amusement as someone approached their table. 'Hallo, Kit,' she said, her smile teasing. 'I wondered how long it would take you to get here.'

Leigh glanced round and met a pair of friendly dark

eyes. The newcomer was a tall, attractive man in his late
twenties, his casual jacket and open-necked shirt giving
him a slightly rakish look when it was combined with the
long, dark brown hair and dark eyes.

'Kit's on our crime desk,' Barbara said to her. 'He's
half Greek, so remember the old proverb and beware if
he comes bearing gifts. He always has an ulterior motive.'

'Stop this sabotage and introduce us,' he said charm-
ingly, smiling down at Leigh, his eyes approving her appearance.

'I wonder if I should,' Barbara said teasingly. 'Leigh's
new to London, and she hasn't got her bearings in this
sinful city yet. I don't think she's up to dealing with you
yet, Kit.'

He gave her a little grin. Turning to Leigh, he said,
'As Ba refuses to play host, let me introduce myself. I'm
Christopher Lianos. And you're the Great White Chief's
new Girl Friday.'

'Leigh West,' she supplied, offering her hand.

He took it and bent to kiss the back of it gracefully.
'How do you spell that?' he asked as he straightened.

She told him and he raised an eyebrow.

'Unusual, but it suits you. No rings, either, I notice,' he
went on wickedly. 'The trouble with Ba is that she's
been wearing that ring on her left hand for so long she's
immune.'

'Very soon now I'll have two on my left hand,' Barbara
said in satisfaction.

'And we'll mourn your absence for the rest of our
lives,' Kit assured her soulfully.

Leigh laughed and he gave her a quick, warm smile.
'So you're new to London,' he said thoughtfully. 'Haven't
seen much of it yet, I suppose?'

'Careful,' Barbara said softly. 'Here comes the propo-
sition!'

He grinned. 'I just wondered if Leigh would like a guide to the fleshpots of London tonight,' he protested. 'Dinner, the cinema ... a native's eye view of the great metropolis.'

Leigh smiled at him. 'Thank you, but I'm still settling into my new flat and I have a lot to do.'

'Tomorrow night?' he asked, undeterred. 'Or on Wednesday?'

Barbara gave Leigh a sparkling glance. 'He's the original bloodhound when he's on the trail of an unattached pretty girl,' she warned.

Leigh was amused by his direct and cheerful manner, and she thought of her silent flat and her lack of friends in London.

'Well ...' she began, weakening.

'Name the day and time,' he said at once, his face brightening. 'Hey, I might get tickets for the theatre. What sort of show would you like to see?'

'I like straight plays,' Leigh told him. 'Any sort of play, in fact. I love going to the theatre.'

'Then I'll pick out something,' he said. 'Tomorrow?'

'Wednesday,' she said, smiling.

'Give me your address and I'll pick you up,' he offered, getting out a diary and pencil.

'I'll meet you,' she said, thinking quickly. She did not want anyone to know she had a flat in Sam's house. 'I doubt if it will be worth while going home after work.'

'Right,' he said cheerfully. 'I finish at six. What time shall we meet?' He gave her a broad grin. 'Six? In the lobby?'

Leigh was amused again. 'If you like,' she agreed.

He straightened, a look of satisfaction on his face. 'Right, I'll see you on Wednesday, then.'

When he had gone, Barbara began to laugh. 'Quick work, Leigh,' she said. 'He's the best-looking of the reporters and he's unattached. I rather like him, too. He can be a bit flirtatious, but he's a very nice man.'

Leigh smiled. 'I've already discovered that London is a very lonely place,' she said. 'It will be nice to have friends.'

Barbara grinned. 'I doubt if you'll lack for them, Leigh, with a face and figure like yours.'

CHAPTER SEVEN

LEIGH found it easy to adapt to the full routine of the working day in the office. Despite the complicated nature of the work, she was so fascinated by what she was learning about the newspaper industry that she was too interested in what she was doing to find it difficult. Barbara surveyed her on the Wednesday afternoon with a smile. 'You're a natural for this job,' she congratulated her. 'You never flap or lose your temper and you pick things up very quickly. Matt's got himself a jewel of a secretary, and I'll tell him so.'

Leigh noted the use of the christian name curiously. She smiled her gratitude for the compliments and replied, 'I'm enjoying every minute of it.'

'Going out with Kit tonight?' Barbara asked her. 'Still on, is it?'

'Yes,' Leigh agreed. 'He rang this morning to confirm that I was coming.'

'I bet he did,' Barbara grinned. 'He's the envy of the reporters' room. A girl with your looks doesn't often turn up in the canteen here, so Kit got in before anyone else could stake a claim.'

ʾLeigh laughed. 'I'm flattered by all the interest.'

The telephone rang and she moved to answer it, dealing quietly with the query from the advertising office while Barbara watched in approval.

At five-thirty Barbara dashed off to get home, but Leigh stayed in the office, tidying some files, her eyes abstracted. She was wearing a jade green silk dress which she had just bought in Oxford Street. The material clung delicately to her slender body as she moved around the room, the slightly flared skirt swirling around her thighs.

Someone suddenly pushed open the door and she turned in some surprise to find herself confronting Cathy Lord. The other girl stared at her with open hostility.

'So you took the job after all?' the girl asked.

'Mr Hume persuaded me it would suit me,' said Leigh, tongue in cheek, feeling a prickle of irritation at the peculiar mixture of childish vulnerability and feminine spite in the enormous green eyes.

Cathy studied her sullenly. 'You dress very well for a secretary,' she commented, her glance running over the silk dress.

Leigh suppressed a smile. 'I have a date tonight,' she said softly.

The green eyes brightened. 'A date? Oh, I see.'

Seeing that her admission had delighted the girl, Leigh quite deliberately told her, 'I'm going out with one of the crime reporters, Kit Lianos.'

'I don't think I know him,' said Cathy, her brows furrowed. 'Is he attractive?'

'Extremely,' Leigh said with a faint smile.

Cathy smiled fully then, a charming, childlike sweetness in her pretty face. 'You were quick to make friends.'

'Kit is a very forceful young man,' Leigh said lightly.

'I met him in the canteen on my first day and he asked me out on the spot.'

'I'm not surprised,' said Cathy, a faint spark of admiration in her eyes. 'You're very beautiful, aren't you?'

Leigh found something touching in the compliment, as though Cathy were trying to make amends for her earlier rudeness.

'Thank you,' she said, smiling back. 'So are you.'

Cathy blushed. 'I'm not beautiful,' she said in a flat voice. 'I wish I was. If I were I'd be certain of Matt.' Her dark lashes flickered down, her face growing pink. 'He's a very hard man to pin down.'

Leigh froze. She did not want Cathy Lord to discuss Matt with her. She glanced at her watch, saying, 'Oh, good heavens, it's past six, and I promised to meet Kit at six in the lobby. I'm so sorry, Miss Lord. I have to rush. Was there anything I could do for you first?'

'I'm just waiting for Matt,' Cathy said frankly. 'He's getting back from New York some time this evening, I'm not sure when, but he's coming straight here, so I thought I'd be here when he arrives to surprise him.'

Leigh gave her a troubled, compassionate look. 'Well, in that case, I'll leave you if I may,' she said politely.

'Oh, yes, don't keep your date waiting,' Cathy said cheerfully. 'I'll just sit in Matt's office chair and twirl around. I like doing that.'

Leigh's eyes widened. A child, she thought. A pretty, vulnerable, helplessly infatuated child. God help her!

She caught the lift down to the lobby and walked out, her slender body graceful in the jade green silk, her blonde hair smooth behind the calm oval of her face. Kit was standing opposite the lifts, a faint frown on his face. As Leigh stepped out it disappeared and he came forward to greet her, smiling broadly.

'I thought you were standing me up for a moment,' he confessed, lightly.'

'I'm sorry I'm late,' she smiled. 'I was detained.'

'It doesn't matter,' he said, taking her hand. 'You're here, that's all that matters.'

'Are you giving me carte blanche to be late whenever I like?' she teased. 'That's a dangerous thing to do to a woman.'

Kit gave her a teasing smile. 'You're a dangerous woman,' he said softly. 'I can feel my rivals breathing down my neck already. One of the sports writers offered me two tickets for Wimbledon to swop for this date with you.'

Leigh broke into laughter, her blue eyes dancing, and turned to walk across the lobby with him. Her smile vanished as she met Matt's steely grey eyes. He had just come into the building, a briefcase under one arm, and she could feel anger in the set of his body as he looked at them both.

Kit hadn't even noticed him. He was talking lightly about the play they were going to see, his head turned to look at Leigh's face.

As they drew level with Matt she tried to walk past him without a word, her pulses racing violently, but he did not move, forcing her to halt and look at him.

Somehow her voice came out coolly. 'Good evening, Mr Hume.'

Kit looked at him in hurried recognition, chiming in a polite greeting.

Matt barely glanced at him before looking back at Leigh. His face was a cold mask, the grey eyes narrowed. 'How are you settling in, Miss West?' he asked icily.

'Very well, thank you,' she said, although the words cost her an enormous effort.

'Finding your feet in London?' he asked, and beneath

the apparent courtesy she felt the deliberate sting of a barb.

She summoned a smile. 'Oh, yes,' she said, sounding as calm as he did. 'Very much so.'

Matt nodded, gave Kit another glance. 'Going somewhere special, Lianos?' he asked.

'A theatre and dinner,' Kit answered. 'I've appointed myself Leigh's guide to London.'

Matt looked back at her, a chilly smile on his hard mouth. 'How splendid,' he drawled, the faintest flintiness in his voice. 'Well, have a pleasant evening.' He turned to go.

'We will,' Kit said cheerfully, and Leigh felt Matt halt for a mere second, as though he were about to turn and say something. Then he walked across to the lifts and she and Kit went out of the door.

The evening was deeply enjoyable. Kit had spared no expense to get good seats and he took her to a very expensive, very attractive Italian restaurant in the West End of London. Leigh tried hard to enter into the fun of the evening. Kit was a friendly, pleasant companion, and she liked him, but the memory of Matt's cold grey eyes and barbed voice remained within her mind every moment of the time. Had they not met him in the lobby she would have been entirely at her ease, but that brief meeting had ruined the evening for her.

For Kit's sake she pretended to be enjoying herself, however, laughing, talking with him, smiling at him from time to time, listening to his talk of his family and of the paper.

When he took her home it was midnight. They sat outside the house in the dark and Kit turned to look at her, a faintly uncertain look on his attractive face.

'Do I have to shake hands, or are you going to let me kiss you, Leigh?' he asked, a little humorously.

She smiled. 'You make me sound alarming,' she said lightly.

'You are,' he said. 'All evening I've had the feeling you weren't really with me. Is there some chap in the background, Leigh?'

She flushed. 'I'm sorry if the evening was a disappointment, Kit.'

'It wasn't that exactly,' he said quickly. 'You're a very lovely girl and you make a pleasant companion, but I'm not getting through to you, am I?' He gave her a wry grin. 'I'm not complaining. You're something special and I was proud to be with you tonight. It's good for the ego to take out a girl who attracts the attention you do.'

Leigh laughed. 'I like your frankness!'

Kit laughed too. 'At least you're really looking at me now,' he said, then he bent down to kiss her, and she was taken by surprise by the sudden movement, and made no effort to resist.

It was a light, exploratory kiss, and Leigh deliberately did nothing to encourage it, although not resisting. After a moment Kit drew away, making a face.

'Yeah,' he said on a soft sigh.

Leigh was amused by his wry face. 'I've only known you three days, Kit,' she said, as direct as himself. 'What do you expect?'

'Bright lights, fairground music and fireworks,' he said ruefully.

'I must go,' she said, amused. She got out of the car, saying goodnight as she bent to close the door. Kit watched her go up the steps into the house, then drove away.

Leigh quietly went up the stairs to her flat and let herself inside, halting in disbelief as she saw the lamp lit beside an armchair and Matt's lean body lounging in it.

She closed the door and stood there, staring into his icy grey eyes.

'How did you get in here?'

'Sam let me in,' he said grimly.

'I shall have to ask Sam never to do such a thing again,' she said angrily.

'You won't,' he said, rising. 'I told you once never to involve other people in our private war, Leigh, and I meant it.'

She opened the door. 'Get out!'

He pushed it shut, staring into her face with a harshness she had never seen on his features before.

'You took your time getting out of Lianos's car,' he said, his mouth barely parting to speak the words.

She deliberately looked into the grey eyes. 'He was making love to me.'

Matt caught her by the throat, his fingers savage, dragging her towards him. 'Do you think I needed to be told that?' he asked through his teeth. 'My God, you'll use any weapon, won't you, Leigh?' He bent his head and began to kiss her with the same brutal violence he had shown that first day in the lift, forcing her lips to part in yielding consent for him.

Leigh had known from the moment that she walked into the room that this would happen. She had known, she thought blindly, trying to resist him, ever since she saw him in the lobby and met the flint-grey eyes and heard the barbed voice.

She pulled back her head, wincing at the strength he used to compel her to stay in his arms. 'Stop it, Matt ... you've forgotten our agreement, haven't you?'

He loosened her hair until it fell in silken strands around her face, his hand rippling through it, watching the glinting hair fall through his fingers. 'You made that condition to save your face, Leigh,' he said sardonically.

'We both know that. You wanted to take the job, but you were afraid I'd read more into it than you wanted me to . . .'

She slapped him with all her strength across his face, and a white fury came into the grey eyes. His hand flew back before she could move, and the blow knocked her off balance.

He caught her as she fell, lifting her into his arms as if she were weightless. 'Let me go,' she said bitterly, twisting to escape from his arms, aware in terror that he was carrying her into the bedroom. 'No, Matt,' she said, her throat closing. 'No, please . . .'

He silenced her, his kiss deep and sensual, and her eyes shut, her hands ceasing to push against his wide shoulders, their fingers beginning to move restlessly against them instead, sliding towards his neck, tentatively creeping into the silvered black hair.

The kiss deepened. Leigh was floating, her mind ceasing to operate, aroused beyond the point of understanding anything but the rising hunger of her own body. He framed her face within his hands, kissing her lids, her ears, her throat, and for a split second her brain registered the fact that they were lying on the bed without Leigh having any idea how they had got there, but before she could think anything else Matt's mouth had found hers again and she was lost.

As he kissed her, his hands moved over her body. It was not until her dress slid away that she realised what he had been doing, and then she did begin to struggle, protesting bitterly, 'No, let me go!' Matt held her firmly, staring into her wide-open, angry blue eyes.

'I've waited for this for six hours, Leigh,' he said harshly. 'You knew what reaction you'd get if you went out with Lianos.'

Her eyes widened, her lashes quivering.

'Didn't you?' He tilted her chin roughly, making her look at him. 'Didn't you?'

Her pulses were hammering against her temple and in her throat. 'Jealous, Matt?' she asked in a whisper that shook.

He didn't answer, his eyes staring into hers. After a moment he looked down at her body, the white shoulders bared when he pulled off her dress, the small high breasts now partially covered by the deep green lace of her slip. Leigh watched his face, her heart deafening her. Slowly he lowered his dark head. Her eyes closed abruptly as he brushed his mouth very softly over her shoulders, his lips parted so that she could feel the warm inner moisture of his mouth sliding over her skin. He delicately kissed the soft hollow in her throat, his hands smoothly caressing her body, and Leigh gave a smothered murmur of protesting pleasure.

Pushing aside the green lace, his lips moved over the smooth white breasts, and Leigh felt a churning turmoil deep inside her stomach. She was suddenly flaming with responses so deep they seemed to wrench at her like agonising pain. Her head began to twist restlessly, her hands flung out on either side of her body, their fingers curling in clenched passion.

Matt suddenly stopped, raising his head to look at her. 'Open your eyes, Leigh,' he ordered grimly.

Her lids fluttered back, her eyes dazed.

'Is the citadel mine, Leigh?' he asked.

She stared at him, quivering.

'I want to hear you submit, Leigh,' he said, his fingers cruel as they took hold of her face. 'Sooner or later you're going to admit defeat.'

She closed her eyes. 'Yes,' she whispered in bitterness.

'Look at me when you say it,' he commanded.

Groaning, she opened her eyes. 'Yes,' she admitted wearily.

His hands grew warmly caressing, tilting her head. When his mouth came down to her she slid her arms around his neck, total surrender in every inch of her body, shuddering under the impact of his unleashed hunger.

Suddenly he pushed her away and got up. She lay, broken out of the pulsing excitement so abruptly that she was dizzy, watching in confused disbelief as he did up his shirt and pushed it down into his trousers.

He looked at her, his grey glance travelling over the slender curves of her half-dressed body. 'Don't make any more dates with Kit Lianos, Leigh,' he said. 'You have Hume stamped all over you, and if I have to make that clear to every man in the building I will. Do you understand?'

Leigh was shivering as the sensual warmth of his hands and body gave way to the aftermath of humiliation, misery and self-contempt. Trying to retrieve some self-respect, she said, her voice shaky. 'I'm not your personal property!'

His mouth twisted sardonically. 'You've just admitted that you are,' he told her.

'I did nothing of the kind!'

'Do I have to win the battle all over again, Leigh?' he asked wryly. 'The citadel just surrendered we both heard the walls fall down. I haven't taken it yet, but it's mine just the same, and I want no other man within a mile of it.'

She stared at him, bewildered, trying to read the look on the hard face. 'I don't understand you,' she murmured. Just now he could have made love to her without any resistance, yet he had stopped. Why? Was it some sort of cat-and-mouse game intended to break her spirit?

'I'm aware that you don't understand, Leigh,' he said, grimly. 'The day you do, the war ends.'

She sat up and pulled the coverlet around her shoulders, shivering. 'I hate you,' she muttered under her breath.

Matt laughed under his own breath and she looked at him furiously.

'I do,' she said bitterly. 'We agreed that you'd leave me alone. I'm not going to be your mistress, Matt.'

'You'll be whatever I want you to be,' he said coolly.

'You arrogant bastard!' she gasped. Her lids lowered. 'And if the gossip gets to Cathy Lord?'

There was a silence. She looked round at him. Matt was staring at her with speculative eyes.

'Why should it?' he asked softly. 'You're so very discreet, Leigh, the perfect secretary.'

Her flush grew. 'If you lay a hand on me again I'll tell her everything,' she said. 'It's time someone opened her eyes to the sort of man you really are!'

His brows drew together. 'Are you trying to blackmail me, Leigh?'

'No,' she said flatly, 'I'm warning you. It was a mistake for me to take a job with you. I admit, I like the work, but if you refuse to leave me alone you'll leave me with no option but to walk out.'

'Isn't it time you faced the fact that I'll never let you walk out on me, Leigh?' he asked softly. 'One way or another, you're staying.'

'Not as your mistress,' she retorted, shuddering.

He thrust his hands into his pockets, his eyes narrowed on her face. 'I could have made you my mistress just now and you would have done nothing to stop me,' he said. 'But I didn't.'

Her eyes filled with flickering confusion. 'Why?' she asked so shakily the word was practically inaudible.

'Work it out for yourself,' he said grimly, turning towards the door. 'Just get this clear, Leigh. You're staying as my secretary, and you won't be going out with other men. You're my property. Is that understood?'

'No,' she said defiantly.

He gave a wry smile. 'You know you'll do what I tell you,' he said. 'Goodnight, Leigh.'

As he left the flat she rolled on to her face, pounding her pillow with her fists. She was caught in a trap from which there was no escape. She had come to London to work for Matt, intending to punish him for his ruthless selfishness, but that implacable will of his imprisoned her. She should never have allowed herself to come within a mile of him. She had no chance of winning a struggle with him when her own body always fought on his side.

Bitterly she admitted to herself that she had gone out with Kit just to annoy Matt. She had known he would be furious. After seeing him in the lobby she had sensed that he would be waiting for her when she got back, much as her pride and self-respect had refused to allow her to admit the fact, even though it had hovered in her mind during her hours with Kit. By going out with Kit she had deliberately challenged Matt, and she had known he would pick up her gauntlet and respond in some way.

Her plan of revenge had gone wildly astray; her own emotions were too deeply involved. She no longer even wanted to go through with it. She did not want to see the pain in Cathy's eyes. She was too afraid of pain, terrified to stir up the cruel emotion of jealousy.

She stared at the ceiling, her blue eyes wide. Was she jealous of Matt and Cathy Lord? She pictured him with Cathy in his arms, and felt nothing but anger. He had no right to hurt that silly, vulnerable child.

A peculiar, birdlike flutter began in her stomach. Matt had no right to amuse himself with other women. A curious, fixed expression froze her eyes. Why on earth had she phrased it like that? No right ... Her heart began to thud. Matt had no right to do it because he belonged to her. Beneath the powerful surge of desire between them she was aware of a strong, insistent sense of ownership towards him which had nothing to do with any softer emotion like love.

Tonight when he forced her to admit she wanted him he had only been making her put into words what she had known that first day in the lift.

They belonged together. Cathy Lord could never match Matt on the same level. It was not merely a driving sexual hunger which drew them together—at some level in their minds they were curiously similar. She recognised him as her counterpart. They were equals, mentally and emotionally, even when he was dominating her physically.

She remembered how he had said, 'We're more alike than you'll admit,' and how her body had blazed with response at the words, surprising and bewildering her. Now she knew exactly what he meant. They were creatures of the same world, their natures oddly dovetailing. She had felt it during lunch on their way from Leicester, catching sight of them in the mirror, seeing the intimacy and communion of their bodies from a distance.

Restlessly she got off the bed and walked up and down the room, frowning over the problem.

Was she in love with Matt?

She halted, staring at her own reflection in the mirror. No, she thought quickly. No.

She got ready for bed and lay down, the room in darkness, her mind too active to permit sleep, trying to fit the pieces of the puzzle Matt had presented her with together. When sleep did come it was daylight and the birds were singing. Leigh was exhausted when she drove to the office with Sam. He eyed her pale face with concern.

'Late night, Leigh?'

She smiled, a faint movement of her mouth. 'Yes,' she admitted.

Sam was frowning as he drove. 'See Matt last night?' he asked. 'Did I do wrong in letting him into your flat?' She heard the worried note in his voice, and was quick to put his mind at rest.

'Of course not, Sam.' Matt had said she must not involve Sam in their private war, and he was right.

Sam relaxed. 'You shouldn't lose sleep, though, Leigh,' he added. 'You look pretty rough this morning.'

Leigh glanced at him curiously, wondering what he had thought of the fact that Matt had asked him to let him wait in her flat all evening. Sam's face betrayed nothing but concern, yet she suspected that he must realise that the relationship between herself and Matt was hardly that of mere secretary and boss.

Barbara was late again that morning, her eyes dancing as she rushed into the office. 'Only two more days! Thank goodness for that. I can't wait to get away from London traffic.'

Leigh looked up from the cabinet she was thumbing through. 'Have trouble again?'

'I always get caught in traffic jams,' Barbara sighed. 'Did you have a nice evening with Kit?' Her brown eyes frowned as she surveyed Leigh's pale face. 'Hey, you look terrible ... don't tell me Kit got out of hand?'

Matt stood in the doorway behind Barbara, his grey eyes on Leigh's face as she answered in confusion. 'No, of course not. I ... I've got a headache, that's all.'

As she finished speaking Matt moved towards her desk. 'Find the Blatchford files, Miss West, and bring them through to my office, will you? Barbara, find some aspirin and coffee for Miss West.' He turned to go, halting. 'By the way, I've got a working lunch in the board room today. Miss West can sit in to take notes. You can skip it, Barbara.'

'Thank you,' Barbara said gratefully, adding, 'Guest list, Matt?'

'There'll be eight of us,' he said. 'Just myself, Miss West and the editors. It's a policy discussion. I want the European diary scratched   it's getting too thin. The main target will be the business pages, though. They're as compelling to read as the labels on jam jars.'

'Have you notified the kitchens?' Barbara asked.

He nodded. 'I spoke to the supervisor last night. He said he'd throw a meal together.'

When he had gone, Barbara grimaced. 'Knowing our kitchens, those words have a prophetic ring!'

Leigh laughed. 'I thought they pulled out all the stops for the board room meals.'

'If given good notice, they do,' said Barbara. 'Still, as it's only the editors that doesn't matter.'

Leigh laughed. 'They don't count?'

'They only work here,' Barbara said grimly. 'If it was the board of directors the story would be different.'

Leigh glanced at her obliquely. 'Talking about the board of directors, Cathy Lord arrived last night just as I was leaving.'

Barbara grimaced. 'Oh, you met Miss World, did you?'

Leigh's eyes filled with amusement. 'Is that what you call her?'

'That's how she behaves,' Barbara retorted. 'Ever since she left finishing school she's been hanging around here trying to get Matt to notice her, and her airs and graces get on my nerves.' Her eyes sparkled angrily. 'She actually tried to insinuate that there was something between Matt and me. I soon told her to jump in a lake!'

'She's very possessive, is she?' Leigh asked casually,

finding the file Matt had asked for and withdrawing it from the cabinet.

'Possessive?' Barbara made a face. 'Do you know, there was a pretty kid in the typing pool who had the most appalling crush on Matt for months. Once or twice he made the mistake of talking to her as if she was human. It sounds hard, but it can be fatal for someone like him. One night she worked like a slave for him for hours, so Matt took her out to dinner, bought her some flowers ... you know, a gesture of appreciation. He always notices when people work very hard for him. Anyway, Cathy Lord noticed this kid mooning over him, and she kicked up a terrible scene with her darling daddy present. Matt tried to smooth it all over, but the kid had a brainstorm and came in and made a big scene with him too ... I think he'd had enough by then. He got the girl another job in the organisation as far away from him as possible.'

Leigh's eyes were as cold and brilliant as diamonds as she listened. 'Poor kid,' she said coolly, when Barbara had finished speaking.

'I was sorry for her,' Barbara said, shrugging. 'So was Matt. He asked me to speak to her.' A little grin crossed her face. 'I think he found it very embarrassing, and he didn't want to hurt the girl. I tried to talk to her, but she was obsessed. In the end Matt had to cut her out of the picture.'

'Yes,' said Leigh, although the monosyllable was stiffly uttered through cold lips. 'I'd better take this file through.'

'Oh, lord, I forgot your coffee and aspirin!' Barbara exclaimed. 'I'm forgetting everything these days.' She smiled. 'I'll rush and get them now and bring them through to Matt's office. I expect he'd like some coffee too.'

Leigh walked into Matt's office and found him dictating into his audio machine. He switched off after a final sentence, and looked at her, his eyes shrewd.

'You look like a ghost,' he said. 'No sleep, Leigh?'

She sat down, placing the file on his desk. 'The file you asked for, Mr Hume.'

He leaned back, his fingertips on the edge of his desk, swivelling in his chair, his eyes examining her face.

'Come to any conclusions?' he asked.

'About what?'

You know what I'm talking about,' he said tersely.

She looked up and met his eyes coldly. 'I came to the conclusion that I'm here to work as your secretary. If there's nothing else you want me to do now I'll go back and get on with learning my way through the filing system.'

His mouth tightened. 'Very well, Leigh,' he shrugged. 'I can play a waiting game.'

For a few seconds confusion shifted over her face, then she smoothed out the expression, her eyes lowering to her hands. 'If that was all, Mr Hume?'

'Not quite,' he snapped. 'I've an appointment at ten with the working committee from the print unions. You can take notes.'

'Yes, Mr Hume,' she said politely.

As she rose he gave her a grim smile. 'My stamina is better than yours, Leigh. I hope you're prepared for a long siege.'

The telephone rang in the outer office. Remembering that Barbara had gone to get them coffee, she went out to answer it.

It was Kit. 'How are you this morning, Leigh?' he asked brightly on hearing her voice.

'Fine, thank you,' she said, equally brightly, aware that she had left the door open between her office and Matt's.

'Enjoy yourself last night?' he asked, and something in his tone made her guess that he was in the reporters' room, probably surrounded by his colleagues, and eager for her to sound enthusiastic.

A faint smile came into her voice. She was touched by his little-boy need to show off. 'It was fantastic, Kit,' she said softly.

He laughed. 'I'm glad you enjoyed it. How about something different next time? There's a party on Saturday night which might be fun.'

'A party?' Leigh frowned slightly. She heard a faint movement and glanced round, meeting Matt's grey, compelling, angry eyes. Deliberately she said, 'That sounds nice, Kit.'

Matt moved beside her. She stared at him warily while Kit was saying eagerly, 'It starts at nine, but we could have dinner first.'

Matt put a hand under Leigh's chin and wrenched her round to face him. 'No,' he said, his tone granite.

Colour swept up her face. Defiantly she began to speak, but Matt took the phone from her hand and slammed it down.

'How dare you cut me off?' she exploded. 'If I want to go out with Kit I will, and you can't stop me!'

The telephone began to ring again. Leigh moved to pick it up, but Matt was faster. He barked, 'Yes?' into it.

Leigh heard a faint confused mumble. Matt listened coldly, then said, 'Lianos, my secretary is here to work for me, not to amuse the reporters' room. She cannot accept personal calls here.' Then he slammed the phone down.

Leigh was shaking with her anger. 'You had no right to do that!'

'I had every right,' he said tightly. 'Once and for all, Leigh, I will not have you seeing other men. Do you understand me?'

Barbara, a tray in her hands, stopped dead in the doorway, hearing the last part of the sentence, and stared, dumbfounded. Matt, catching Leigh's stricken look towards the door, glared round at Barbara and stalked into his office, slamming the door so that the glass panels shook.

Barbara's eyes sought Leigh's with a dazed query in them. Leigh turned back to her work without a word. After a moment Barbara placed a cup of coffee and some tablets beside her, and Leigh murmured a subdued, 'Thank you.'

Discreetly, Barbara began her own work, making no comment on what she had heard, but for the rest of the morning Leigh caught her puzzled, curious look whenever Barbara thought she was unaware of her.

CHAPTER EIGHT

BARBARA'S last day was hectic. Matt presented her with a wedding present from the staff, a beautiful set of bedlinen which she seemed delighted with, and made a little speech to her in the board room while a crowd of people listened and then applauded. She laughed, her face flushed with excitement, then bent and kissed Matt quickly, her eyes teasing.

'Thank you,' she said. 'I'm not going to make a speech. I hate them. Just ... thank you, all of you.'

Leigh stood at the back of the room, feeling excluded from the staff chatter, realising that this was Barbara's moment, and she was best out of it so that she might enjoy the centre of the stage.

Everyone had a glass of champagne, courtesy of the management, and Barbara whirled around talking to everyone, sparkle in her eyes and a smile on her mouth.

After a while Leigh slipped out and went back to the office to cope with the work. The day went on somehow. Matt came back, gave her a cool look, and went into his office to begin making long telephone calls.

The building throbbed with activity below them. Far in the bowels of the earth the printing presses thundered, the printers hot and sweating, moving from machine to machine, their aprons filthy. Vans drove in and out of the car park to collect parcels of papers. The telephones rang. People trooped through to talk to Matt and came back, nodding to Leigh.

Barbara came back, having said all her goodbyes, and had a brief chat. 'I'm sure you've already got the hang of everything, but I've left that absolute pile of notes which you can consult if need be ... It's a good idea to keep it up to date, just in case you leave in a hurry and someone has to take over.'

Leigh gave her a curious look, noting the tone. What did Barbara think of what she had overheard?

Matt wandered through in shirt sleeves, his collar open, and a tired look on his face. He talked to Barbara for a moment, smiling at her. 'Every good wish for the wedding. I'll try to get down for it, I promise, but you know this business ...'

'I'd like you to be there,' said Barbara. 'Try, Matt.' She collected all her things, giving the office a last glance. 'Oh, well, keep the ship afloat,' she said brightly.

When she had gone Leigh tidied her desk, aware that Matt was standing watching her. Now that she had stopped work she was aching from head to foot. The pressures of the last two days were killing. She had to work at full stretch to keep up, and she was not surprised Barbara was relieved to give up the job. It would not be possible to combine it with running a home.

'Dinner?' Matt asked lazily, rubbing a hand over the back of his neck.

Leigh shook her head, collecting her bag and a wicker basket of shopping she had bought in her lunch hour. 'I think I'll have a bath and get to bed,' she said.

He moved into her path. 'You aren't planning on going to that party tomorrow, are you?' There was menace in the cold voice.

'I'm your secretary, nothing else,' she said rebelliously. 'My private life is my own affair.'

He took her elbow in a compelling grip. 'Come into my office. I want to talk to you.'

'I'm tired, Matt,' she protested, but he pulled her after him, despite her weary tone, and closed the door behind them.

Leigh faced him, her chin defiant. Matt stared at her, still rubbing the back of his neck, his chin showing a faint dark stubble. There was grim weariness in his grey eyes.

'Leigh, didn't what happened with your ex-fiancé teach you anything?' he asked her flatly. 'You're no more attracted to Lianos than you are to Sam. He's a pleasant companion, no doubt, but you and I both know that there's no future in it.' He sounded almost bored as he spoke, his tone dry. 'If you get involved with the boy, you'll hurt him. For God's sake, leave him alone!'

She flushed. 'You make it sound as though I were pursuing him!'

Matt grimaced. 'You don't have to, Leigh. A sideways look gets any man you want, doesn't it?'

She felt her pulses flutter and lowered her lashes. 'I'm not a femme fatale.'

'Aren't you?' His voice was grim. 'I'd say that's just what you are. In your cool, quiet way you demolished that fiancé of yours. I saw from the start just how you could make him jump with one look, and you know I saw very clearly. You told me you felt guilty about what you did to him.'

'I do,' she protested, her eyes bitter. 'I never wanted to hurt him ...'

'Then leave Lianos alone. He's not for you, any more than the other man was ... you'll only hurt him, too, and weep when you can't put the pieces back together again.'

She flinched. 'You make me sound vile!'

He smiled grimly. 'Cruel, Leigh ... a cruel, beautiful little cat with sharp claws. Every man who looks at you wants to stroke that soft silky coat of yours, and sometimes you let them for a moment, only to dig those sharp claws of yours into their flesh and tear them to pieces afterwards.'

'No,' she said harshly. 'Don't talk about me like that!'

Matt stared at her. 'I have to,' he said levelly. 'You seem to be unable to make these decisions for yourself. If you don't want to reduce young Lianos to the same desperate state you brought your fiancé to, keep away from him. And from anyone else who looks at you.'

'Including you?' she asked softly, her lashes lowered.

There was a silence. She looked at him through her lashes and saw his hard, tired face in the glint of late afternoon sunlight, a weary smile on his mouth, the lines of laughter, pain, experience pulling his brown skin into a cast of wry resignation.

'I'm different,' he said. 'I've never suffered from the same illusions about you, Leigh. Try to use your claws on me and I'll hurt you back.' He moved suddenly, taking her by the shoulders. 'Unlike the others, Leigh, I do know how to hurt you back, don't I?'

She quivered, looking up into his hard face. 'I won't let you,' she said huskily.

He gave that weary smile. 'My God, I'm too tired to argue with you tonight,' he sighed. 'It's been a difficult week. Stop arguing, Leigh. Just tell me what I want to hear.'

She hesitated, biting her lip. At that moment they both heard footsteps approaching her office. Matt released her suddenly, pushed open the door between his office and her own. She stared at him, puzzled. Turning back to her, he looked at her oddly, a glint in his grey eyes.

'Leigh!'

She heard Kit's voice as he walked through the door of her office, but before she could answer, Matt had pulled her hard into his arms and his mouth found hers, compelling her response, his hands on her back, forcing her to yield.

She heard Kit's step halt. Matt's hands slid up to the back of her head, tilting her face backward. Leigh closed her eyes, shivering. After a moment Kit's footsteps quietly walked away. As he closed the door of her office Matt released her.

She looked up at him, her eyes brilliant in her face. He surveyed her with a mocking smile.

'Very clever, Matt,' she said huskily. 'But doesn't it occur to you that letting one of your own reporters see that was a stupid mistake? Within half an hour it'll be all round the building.'

'I told you I'd stamp Hume on you so that everyone knew exactly what the situation was,' he retorted coolly.

'Including Miss Cathy Lord?' she asked tersely.

Matt's eyes narrowed. 'I'd forgotten Cathy,' he said, almost to himself.

'I'm sure she'd be pleased to hear that,' said Leigh.

Matt gave her a strange, oblique look. 'You look as tired as I feel, Leigh. I'll drive you home.'

'No, thank you,' she said.

'I've had enough of your arguments for one day,' he drawled, his voice bored. 'Just do as I say, Leigh. My head aches and I've got an iron band around the back of my neck.'

'I hope it throttles you!' she snapped, walking out of the office.

He caught her up at the lifts and they went down to the car park in silence. As he slid her into the passenger seat of his car she caught a glimpse of Kit in a small sports car, watching them, his face shadowed. Beside him sat another reporter with a faint grin on his face.

Leigh looked down at her hands. Matt got in beside her and gave her a quizzical look. 'Get used to it, Leigh,' he said softly. 'By Monday they'll all know.'

'You're insane!' she muttered under her breath.

He started the engine and the long limousine purred towards the exit. Leigh could feel Kit's eyes on them every inch of the way. She was relieved when they shot out into the daylight and the roar of Fleet Street traffic.

Matt stopped outside Sam's house and looked at her. 'If you were a Good Samaritan you'd give me some aspirin and a cup of tea,' he said blandly. 'My head is splitting.'

'I'd be more likely to bury a hatchet in your scalp,' she said tartly, trying the door handle.

He followed her up the steps and Leigh eyed him irritably. 'Matt, go home and get some sleep. You look worn out.'

He gave her a charming, pleading smile. 'All I want is a cup of tea,' he said softly.

She sighed. 'You're impossible!'

As they entered the house Sam came out of the kitchen, halting as he saw Matt behind her. Leigh saw the odd look on Sam's face smooth out quickly into discreet courtesy.

'How are you, Matt?' he asked.

'Exhausted,' said Matt, rubbing a hand around his neck again. 'Leigh's going to dose me with aspirin.'

Sam glanced at her, then nodded and vanished back into his own rooms. Leigh walked up the stairs, her cheeks flushed. What on earth was Sam going to think when he heard the gossip on Monday?

In her flat she went to the kitchen to put the kettle on, while Matt lay down on the small modern couch, his head on a cushion, his eyes wearily closed.

Leigh made tea and went back to him with a tray. He lay very still, his features smoothed out in a vulnerable expression. The regular breathing warned her that he had fallen asleep. She put the tray down and tiptoed into her kitchen, closing the door very quietly.

She prepared a liver and kidney casserole and slid it into the oven, then began to clean and prepare a salad, which she placed in the tiny refrigerator.

Moving softly around the kitchen she did some more work, before quietly returning to the sitting-room. Matt still slept, his face turned against the cushion, his silvered black hair ruffled. Leigh sat down in a chair, her feet under her, and leaned back, watching him. Suddenly she heard footsteps on the stairs, and shot up, moving to her front door before anyone could knock.

As she opened it she saw Mrs Sam, her eyes concerned, bearing a plate of shortcake in her hands. Leigh put a finger to her lips. 'Matt's fallen asleep,' she whispered, gesturing to the couch. 'He just sat down and went out like a light.'

Mrs Sam's face softened. 'Poor lamb,' she said, and

Leigh's heart turned over at the expression. It was so odd used about Matt.

'I brought up this shortcake for his tea,' Mrs Sam added, handing her the plate. 'He loves it.'

'Thank you,' Leigh whispered. 'I don't like to wake him, he's so tired.'

Mrs Sam gave her another odd look, and nodded. 'You're right,' she whispered. 'If he goes home there's only that man who runs the flat for him and he's no use to man or beast. Oh, he does the work, but he's a stiff sort of fellow. There's nobody to make Matt stop working when he's worn out.' She turned to go. 'Will you be all right with him, Leigh?' The question was casual, but Leigh could sense the curiosity behind it.

'Yes,' she said, her tone noncommittal. 'Thank you, Mrs Sam.'

Leigh closed the door quietly and returned to her chair. Matt went on sleeping, the hard lines of his face relaxed and softened. The room darkened. She did not like to put on any light in case it woke him. The warmth of the summer light faded, leaving her chill. She would have liked to switch on an electric fire, but that too might disturb him. At one point she went into the kitchen and turned down the casserole to simmer slowly. A delicious fragrance filled the room. Her stomach clamoured for food, but she went back to Matt, closing the door.

He woke up a while later, turning restlessly, his head falling back against the leather couch arm. He opened his eyes, frowning, and for a moment his face was confused. Leigh watched him, curled up in her chair like a little girl, her head on her knees.

His eyes peered through the shadowy room towards her. She wondered in amusement if he remembered where he was, then his voice said lazily, 'Let down your golden hair, Leigh.'

She laughed. 'You've slept for two hours. Feel better?'

He stretched, his arms above his head, the long hard muscles of his lean body tightening. Leigh's heart gave a flip inside her breast. She got up to hide the momentary response.

'I've got a liver casserole in the oven. Hungry?'

'Ravenous,' he said.

She went into the kitchen, switching on a lamp so that the room was filled with soft light, dispelling the dark shadows. While she was serving the meal she heard Matt moving in the room, and when she moved back, carrying warm plates, the casserole and the salad on a tray, she found he had switched on the fire and drawn the curtains. The room looked quite different now, filled with warmth and light. Matt began to lay the small dining table in the window alcove and she laid out the dinner in the centre.

'We ought to have some wine,' he said, seating her.

She gave him a wry look. 'Be grateful for getting anything,' she said tartly.

He grinned at her, his eyes caressing. 'Thank you for letting me sleep, Leigh. You were tired too. You still look tired.'

She served the meal, the fragrant odour of the casserole making her nostrils quiver with hunger. They ate in comparative silence, the atmosphere peaceful between them. The accustomed tension of his presence in the same room seemed to have seeped away during the evening. She felt oddly at home, her mind and body relaxed.

They washed up together, moving around the small kitchen, their eyes meeting occasionally. Afterwards Matt went into the sitting-room and found her cassette player, sliding a cassette into the compartment. Leigh stood in the doorway, watching as he stretched out on the couch, his legs lazily relaxed, his hands behind his head. He patted the seat beside him silently, returning his hand to rest beside his chair.

Leigh felt a reluctant quiver of unrest, eyeing him. He grinned at her, reading her expression. 'I'm going in half an hour,' he said. 'Sit down and relax, Leigh. You're tired and so am I.'

She sat down, her body poised for escape. The rich soft sounds of Brahms stole across the room. Matt's arm uncoiled and fell across her shoulders, pulling her closer, his hands pushing her blonde head down against his chest. For a brief second she was on the point of resistance, but he was right: she was too tired. She sighed, relaxing against him, her legs automatically curling up underneath her in a posture of total comfort. His hand gently fiddled with her pins, releasing her hair. She smiled faintly.

'Leave my hair alone.'

'It's like the golden shower of Danae,' he said, running his fingers through it. 'Fine gold gleaming in the firelight.'

'I would never have called you romantic, Matt,' she commented, turning her cheek against him so that she could look into his face.

He dropped a light kiss on her nose. 'Men are always romantic at heart. They just hate women to find out. Women are the hard-headed half of the race.'

'Do you like Brahms?' she asked, finding the warmth of his body against her deeply seductive.

'Very much,' he said, his hands playing with her hair. He lifted a great swathe of it, his mouth brushing it. 'Is it the shampoo you use that makes your hair smell of flowers?'

'What sort of flowers?' she asked, her lids closing.

'Roses and violets,' he said, his lips moving over her temples.

She chuckled. 'I wash it in egg and lemon, actually.'

He groaned. 'As I said, women are the hard-headed ones.'

'Wrong answer, Matt?' she asked sleepily.

'Wrong answer,' he agreed, shifting his body slightly so that her head fell across his lap into the crook of his arm. She blinked lazily, surprised, and saw the dark mask of his face staring down at her.

'I'm so sleepy, Matt,' she whispered.

'I know,' he said softly. His face descended and her lids closed. Their mouths touched lightly. Her lips parted without any pressure from him and her arms slid up to hold his neck, pulling him closer. The kisses were gentle, sensuous, exquisitely soft. Without passion, Leigh surrendered to the comfort of the slow movements of his mouth, soothed to the point of sleep. Her response grew more and more languid. Matt drew back and looked at her cool oval features, his hands pushing back the fine shimmering hair.

Leigh breathed deeply once, then tried to open her eyes. He picked her up in his arms and walked with her into the bedroom. She staggered as he placed her on the bed and he supported her.

'Just sit still,' he said gently. She felt his hands moving over her and forced her lids open.

'Matt, no!'

'You're too damn tired to undress yourself,' he said mockingly. He removed her dress and shoes, but she had dragged herself back to a vague state of awareness, and hurriedly pulled away.

'I can do the rest,' she said firmly.

He laughed, looking at her oddly. 'Goodnight, Leigh. I'll let myself out,' he said, bending to kiss her.

She accepted the kiss softly, her lashes flickering on her cheek. He walked to the door and she watched him, seated on the bed, her long silken hair flowing over her naked shoulders. Matt looked back and she felt the shaft of desire in his eyes. Then he went out without a word and Leigh sighed.

That night something seemed to have shifted the balance of their relationship. Leigh returned to work on the following Monday, finding herself, as she had feared, the object of many curious, speculative glances, and waited for Matt's appearance with a sense of apprehension. When he came into the office, darkly elegant in his formal suit, he glanced towards her, a faint smile on his face, his eyes warm.

'Good morning, Leigh. Pleasant weekend?'

'Yes, thank you. Did you?' She made the obvious response slightly hesitantly. She had half expected all weekend to hear from him, but he had made no sign.

'Super,' he sighed. 'I went down to see my parents.'

'Oh?' She knew nothing much about his family. Her only glimpses had come from Mrs Sam's rambling gossip about him.

'They live in Hampshire,' he told her. 'Just beyond the New Forest. It's a very peaceful place, isolated enough to be very quiet, but near enough to Christchurch for shopping and sailing.'

'Sailing?' Leigh looked at him in surprise. 'Do you sail?'

'I've a boat at Christchurch,' he said. 'When I can get down there I like to sail for a few hours. It's relaxing, a different sort of struggle.'

She looked obliquely at him. 'You enjoy conflict, don't you, Matt?'

He gave her a mocking little smile. 'It's the breath of life to me,' he said softly.

The telephone rang and she answered it. Her voice was cool as she recognised the caller. 'Of course, Miss Lord, I'll put you through at once.'

She turned her head to glance at Matt in silence.

He gave her a curious little smile, his eyes unreadable, and went through to his own office, closing the door. Leigh put Cathy Lord through to him and got on with her work.

Once the avalanche of the day had started it never seemed to stop. She was kept working flat out from the moment she arrived until the time she left.

Her relationship with Matt was as quietly intimate as if they were old friends. He talked to her easily, confidentially. He trusted her judgment when he had some problem to unravel. They worked in total harmony together day after day.

Leigh knew perfectly well that gossip about them was circulating freely. She no longer ate in the canteen because she found the ordeal of being so scrutinised unbearable.

Some days she brought in a pre-packed lunch to eat in the office if she knew she would be very busy. Some days she ate in the board room when Matt had a working lunch. Once or twice he broke off at one o'clock and said casually, 'Let's eat out, Leigh.' Without protest she would eat lunch with him at a quiet restaurant, their talk always of work.

She had ceased to make sense of what was happening between them. She had ceased to make plans to punish him for what he had done to Ann. She existed day by day in a state of abeyance, as though she did not know where life would carry her next.

Cathy Lord came into the office from time to time, polite but guarded with Leigh, and it was clear that she had not as yet heard any of the gossip which was rife in the building. It was only a matter of time, Leigh thought wryly. What would Matt do then?

It occurred to her at times that he might plan to erase her from his life as ruthlessly as he had done Ann, but the prospect was not somehow convincing. Leigh watched him as he talked to Cathy, his arm around the girl's slender shoulders, and felt an ache of pity for the adoring, vulnerable young face lifted to gaze at him. She knew in the depths of her being that Cathy had never once seen Matt as she had seen him. The relationship was unequal. Cathy was out of her class with him; she had no idea at all of his true nature. The glamour of his image clung about him whenever those bright green eyes gazed at him. Yet Leigh knew that the image he projected outwardly was only a shadow of the man, not the man himself.

Leigh winced at the idea of how Cathy would feel when she heard the gossip about Matt and herself. She had no more wish to hurt the girl than she would have had if it had been her cousin Ann.

The weeks went by and summer faded into autumn. Leigh was so accustomed to the office work that she found it less and less of a strain to cope with the pressures it daily laid upon her. In September, Cathy Lord flew to America for a month to visit her uncle in San Francisco. Leigh was relieved at the news. It delayed the moment when Cathy would burst out with jealous accusations.

The long hours she spent in Matt's company had their own brand of delight. She enjoyed working with him, and was gradually able to lift some of the routine burden from his shoulders by sifting through the piles of paperwork which came into the office each day, deciding whether he needed to read it or not, and compiling a brief list of the contents of memos and letters so that he could see at a glance what was going on in the organisation.

Their lunches together were more and more frequent. If Matt was not attending some necessary business function, they habitually ate out. Several evenings in the week he drove her home and came into the flat to eat dinner she cooked. Afterwards they sat on the couch and listened to music by the firelight, her head on his lap while he stroked her loosened hair.

'It's a very relaxing occupation,' he said mockingly, smiling down at her. 'Better than worry beads.'

'Thanks,' she said, tongue in cheek. 'Perhaps I should patent it. I'd make a fortune from tired business men.'

A gleam came into his eyes. 'I've no doubt you would, but I might have something to say about that.'

'You have something to say about everything,' she retorted.

He cupped her face in his warm hands and kissed her in that slow, sensuous fashion which turned her blood to fire and made her totally pliant in his arms.

The evenings always seemed to end the same way. Matt would make love to her with disturbing precision until she was almost crazy, then he would get up to go, leaving her aching with angry frustration.

One night, after he had got up, raking down the ruffled silvery dark hair, she burst out huskily, 'What are you doing to me, Matt? Trying to break my spirit?'

His hands lowered from his hair. He looked at her penetratingly. 'Is that what I'm doing, Leigh?' he asked oddly.

'I don't know what you think you're doing,' she said furiously. Her face was flushed and bitter as she stared back at him. 'You're driving me out of my mind!'

His eyes narrowed. 'Why?' he asked, the question dropping very quietly.

She got up and walked restlessly to the fireplace. 'Oh, forget it,' she said thickly. 'Goodnight, Matt.'

'Answer my question,' he said, moving behind her.

She shook her head.

His hand turned her to face him, his fingers gripping tightly at her shoulder. 'Why am I driving you out of your mind, Leigh?'

'You know perfectly well why,' she said huskily.

'You tell me.'

'Why should I tell you what you know already?'

'I want to hear it,' he said, shaking her slightly.

She took a long, deep breath. 'I think it's time we stopped this,' she said levelly. 'It's gone on long enough.'

His eyes hardened. 'If it has to go on for the rest of your life, I'll break you, Leigh,' he said, and the stark statement sent the blood rushing out of her face.

She stared at him, her blue eyes almost dark in the whiteness of her face. He had admitted it.

Her chin rose. Her mouth set hard. Quietly, she said, 'You'd better go, Matt.'

He stared at her, his eyes narrow and restless. 'I wish I could take off the top of that beautiful head and see what's going on inside it,' he said, almost to himself. 'You're an expert on camouflage, aren't you, Leigh? God knows what's going on behind that exquisite cameo of a face.'

'We're two of a kind, you told me,' she said flatly. 'I don't understand you, either, Matt.'

There was a curious look of consideration about his features, as though he were debating a course of action which troubled him.

His eyes tried to probe into her guarded glance, but she showed him nothing but a level stare.

'Goodnight, Matt,' she said again.

He moved to the door, giving her a last, odd look before he left. Alone, Leigh sat down on the carpet in front of the fire and laid her cold white face on her bent knees, her hair loosely flowing over her hands. Tears began to trickle slowly down her face.

As if they had been damned for centuries, they grew rapidly, until she was broken with sobbing, her body shaking with it. She cried until she was weary, the firelight gleaming over her white, wet face.

She did not ask herself the cause of those endless, necessary tears. They had been waiting at the back of her mind for a long time. When they were over she got ready for bed and fell asleep at once.

The autumn sunlight dappled the office next morning, lying in chequered patterns on furniture and walls. Leigh worked quietly, her face as calm and contained as if she had never cried so helplessly the night before.

Matt came in, shot her a guarded, penetrating look and went into his own office. The telephone began its clamour. The procession of visitors began. Leigh was grateful for the necessity of concentrating on her daily routine.

Matt called her into his office later that afternoon to take some notes while they both listened to a tape of a conversation he had had that morning. 'I feel I've missed the weak link somewhere,' he said impatiently. 'Somewhere he said something essential, and I missed it.'

They listened to it twice before Leigh said suddenly, 'Wait a minute . . . turn back about a dozen sentences.'

Matt wound the tape back and they listened again. She looked at him. 'You noticed that? There's some indecision when he's talking about the negotiations. Maybe the committee aren't unanimous, after all.'

Matt leant back, throwing a pencil across the table. 'That's it! I knew I'd caught the whiff of something.' He smiled at her wearily. 'I've been puzzling about it all day. Of course, he tried to hide it from me, but it was there all right.'

Suddenly the door was flung open and Cathy Lord came into the office, her face deeply flushed, a wild, furious look in her green eyes. Leigh took one look and her heart was squeezed in pain.

The girl's voice was jerky with jealousy and temper.

'Matt, is it true? Don't lie to me. You and her ... for months, they said. Oh, Matt, how could you? It's ... it's horrible!' She looked at Leigh with violent bitterness. 'You're his mistress. All these months, pretending to be so cool and polite, and you're his mistress!' She turned back to Matt, tears in her green eyes. 'I detest you ... I think you're disgusting! When Daddy hears he'll ...' Her words broke off, her mouth quivering. 'He'll hate you, too,' she ended flatly.

Leigh got up and moved towards the door, but Cathy flew at her like a wildcat, her fingernails raking Leigh's smooth cheek. Matt made a sound under his breath and caught the girl back. Blood running down her white face, Leigh looked at him almost blankly, then went out of the room.

She heard Cathy's wild sobbing and Matt's soft murmured response, a gentle soothing note in his voice.

The cloakroom was empty when she went in there. She washed her face, dried it and tried to cover the long scratches with powder, but they still showed. She returned to her office in a state of trance, collected her things and quietly walked out. In Matt's office she could hear Cathy crying and Matt talking gently to her.

Leigh took the lift down to the car park and went out that way, grateful for the shadows which hid her face from curious eyes. A bus halted in the traffic jam nearby. Instinctively, she got on it and went up the stairs. She sat down and stared out of the window, a totally numb feeling inside her head.

CHAPTER NINE

THE bus took her to Hampstead Heath. Recognising her whereabouts, she decided on an impulse to get off and walk across the wild heathland, under the vibrant beauty of the autumnal trees. Her feet shuffled through oceans of dry leaves, their colour merging from vivid red to dull brown, the sound of her movements through them coming to her ears with a dry whisper. A grey squirrel ran across her path, bushy tail frisking, and darted up a great beech tree. The black and white of a magpie shot across the span of a barrel-girthed oak, its bare branches black against the sky.

Leigh leaned against the oak trunk, feeling the slight warmth of the sun held within the bark, and stared into the trees. The emptiness which had received her when Cathy Lord burst out with her jealous misery seemed to hold her even now. She had had to get away. She did not analyse why—she only responded to the deep impulse to escape.

Cathy's young face had been twisted with emotion, she thought, shivering. Emotion destroyed. It hurt. Leigh had been unable to stay there and see the pain in the girl's eyes. She had been moved by pity, anger, fear.

The faint warmth of the afternoon was ebbing. The sky lost colour gradually, and she began to be aware of a chill in the autumn air.

She had stayed still for so long that the birds were ignoring her, their evening search for food before night fell growing more urgent, hopping and flying around the stiff human figure without noticing her. Their flight calls had a melancholy sound. It chimed with the slow grey descent of the evening.

Unconsciously she was thinking deeply about the situation in which she found herself. She had been avoiding the making of any decision for weeks. The need for a decision had been clear enough to her, but she had preferred to let things drift, vaguely knowing that the explosion which had come that day must come some time, yet preferring to wait for it rather than to run away.

She sighed deeply. She had to run away, she admitted starkly; she had known that for a long time. Matt was only too well aware of her response to him. She did not understand why he was playing this waiting game, but he had made it clear that sooner or later he would take what she could no longer refuse him. A wry grimace twisted her face. She had never been able to refuse him, she admitted bitterly. From the first day they met he had known he could walk in and demand her surrender without resistance.

The puzzle of his behaviour still confused her. She wished vainly that she understood him. Failing that, she had no choice but to go, and go fast and far before he caught up with her. She did not doubt that Matt would follow her. Whatever the reasoning behind his long delay in taking the citadel he had called his property, she was under no illusions. He would not let her go. She would have to escape before he guessed her intention.

It was late dusk before she moved, her body reluctant. She took a bus back to Sam's house and cautiously viewed the house. There was no sign of Matt's car outside, but she knew his devious mind too well not to be afraid he would be waiting in her flat.

She slowly opened her flat door and at once became

aware of the fragrance of cigar smoke. A tense stiffness seized her and she looked quickly around the room. In an ashtray a crushed cigar butt lay cold and buried in ash. Quickly she looked into the other rooms, sighing with relief when she realised Matt had gone. He had been there. Leigh eyed the ashtray. How long had he waited? She could imagine his mood.

Bolting the door with a chain bolt, she hurriedly began to pack. It took her half an hour to gather everything she needed, and she realised she would need a taxi to the station.

She had originally intended to go to Leicester, but on second thoughts had realised that Matt could easily find her there. Searching her mind for boltholes she had come up with her Aunt Ellen in York, a relative she rarely saw but with whom she had always had a very good relationship. Aunt Ellen would offer her temporary shelter until she found a flat and a job in York, and Matt, for all his quick tongue and domineering manner, would find it hard to browbeat her parents in order to discover her whereabouts.

Before she left, though, she must speak to Sam and Mrs Sam, apologising for her sudden departure. It would cause them much inconvenience, and she regretted upsetting them.

She rang for a taxi to arrive in ten minutes, then went down to speak with Mr and Mrs Sam. She could hear their television as she approached their sitting-room, and tapped on the door. Sam looked at her in odd reproach. 'Where have you been, Leigh?' he asked. 'Matt was here looking for you. He waited for two hours, but he had to go back to the Gazette.' His face was grave. 'A strike has started—the machine minders have got the bit between their teeth. It looks bad. A long stoppage could ruin the firm. Matt's very worried.'

Leigh looked at him with concern. A long wrangle with the men who watched the print machines had been going on for weeks over the manning agreement which guaranteed so many men to work with so many machines. Leigh knew the background to the strike, but she had not anticipated that one would start, since the official union attitude was not in sympathy with the chapel responsible.

Mrs Sam saw her worried, uncertain expression, and touched her arm, her small bird-like fingers gentle. 'He was here when they rang with the news of the strike, Leigh. He looked so tired. He needs you.'

Leigh's blue eyes stared into the older woman's face. Mrs Sam looked back persuasively. 'Go back to the office, Leigh. He has a lot on his plate just now. Don't make it worse for him.'

Leigh's shoulders sagged. She nodded without replying. The square box of the television was blaring the news and suddenly she caught sight of the Gazette building, a sea of angry, shouting faces surrounding it. Matt was shouldering his way through them. The grey vision blurred his face as though he were a million miles away, but even in that poor reproduction she could see the weary tension in his hard face and in the lines of neck, shoulders, body as he tried to reach the door.

Sam and his wife had fallen silent, watching as closely as she did. The news reader switched to another item and they both looked at Leigh.

Her taxi arrived at that moment. She walked to the door with Mrs Sam softly saying, 'Make sure he eats something, Leigh—I don't suppose he's even thought of it. Even a glass of milk would be better than nothing at all.'

The taxi seemed to take forever to arrive in the evening London traffic jams. Leigh sat on the edge of the seat, willing the vehicle to move faster. Her own panic and fear had evaporated at the instant that she saw Matt's tired face on the television. However much it hurt her, she had to be there in case he needed her. He had rubbed a hand around the back of his neck in that characteristic gesture of his, his eyes grim, and her heart had moved involuntarily with love.

She closed her eyes, wincing. Love, she thought dully. Oh, God, I love him. All these years she had evaded the glittering trap emotion laid for her, only to fall into it at last without even noticing. The wild desire she had felt for him from their first meeting had been a separate issue. Passion was not as dangerous as love. It could humiliate, irritate, even infuriate, but it could not wound as deeply as love could. Love was the ache beyond remedy which had been nagging at her for days, even weeks. She had refused to admit it to herself because of her fear of it.

She asked the taxi driver to drop her outside the car park entrance, and walked through there to the lifts to escape the press of waiting men outside the main entrance. When she arrived at the top floor she found an atmosphere of tension. A couple of girls were sitting in the typing pool, talking; the others had all gone home. Leigh nodded to them without speaking as she passed, feeling their curious, fascinated gaze on her. She stopped in her own office and rapidly tidied her hair, applied fresh make-up and checked her appearance. She had a peculiar intuition that she must look as normal as possible. The scratches Cathy had inflicted on her had faded to a dull red, and she carefully camouflaged them to the best of her ability. During her time at the flat she had changed into a smooth, tight-fitting black suit under which she wore a white silk blouse with a rollneck collar which gave her a cool, elegant look.

When she felt able to carry it off, she opened the door of the board room, finding the air thick with smoke and the stale odour of beer. Matt sat the head of the long table, in his shirtsleeves, his collar open, his tie discarded. Men sat facing each other on each side. There were about a dozen in all, she saw at a glance.

At her quiet entrance Matt's glance flickered towards the door. He looked tense and strained, a whiteness around his mouth. The grey eyes widened as he saw her. He had been talking, but for a few seconds the brisk flow of language halted. The men turned their heads to look at her.

Without speaking, she moved round the room and pushed a chair into a position slightly behind Matt, sitting down, her pad open on her knee. He glanced round briefly. The strained whiteness seemed to have faded from around his mouth. He turned back to the other men and began to speak again.

Leigh recognised some of the men facing her. Her eyes flitted over their faces, noting the presence of the Father of the Imperial Chapel, the main co-ordinating body which linked all the separate union chapels at the firm. A large, square-faced man with a jutting chin he was listening calmly to Matt, while opposite him sat one of the Chief executives of the Gazette, his tie crooked, a wrinkled jowl giving him the melancholy look of a wattled turkey when he talked excitedly. Nearest to Matt sat Pete Turner, the Father of the striking chapel, his face obstinate. A few beads of perspiration clung to his receding brown hair and he was looking irritable.

Leigh glanced discreetly at her watch. Nine o'clock. Had Matt eaten anything since lunchtime? Had the others? She looked down the table, seeing glasses standing among the litter of paper, pens, newspapers, sheafs of notes.

There was no sign of any food.

Pete Turner was talking hotly, the sweat on his forehead gleaming. Matt leaned his elbows on the table, listening. Leigh scribbled a note and passed it to him discreetly. He read it at a glance, turned and nodded to her.

She got up and quietly went out. In her own office she rang the canteen and ordered sandwiches, coffee and beer to be sent up to the board room. When they arrived ten minutes later she helped the canteen girl to carry them into the board room and distribute them. There were grateful glances from all the men at the sight of the food. They began to eat, talking as they did so, and Matt absently followed suit. She had ordered a cold glass of milk for him too, and when she put it in front of him he gave it a disgusted look, pushing it away. Leigh calmly placed it in front of him again. Pete Turner, who was talking bitterly, paused, watching them. Matt looked at Leigh sideways, a grim expression on his face. Her blue eyes met his glance calmly. He picked up the milk with a wry face and drained it at a gulp. Pete Turner suddenly chuckled, and the other men laughed, too. Matt gave them all a rueful look.

There was a faint pause, as though the tiny incident had thrown them off balance, then the hard negotiations began again. Leigh sat back, listening, watching the weary droop of Matt's shoulders.

The clock ticked on. Voices rose and fell. The smoky atmosphere deepened. Pete Turner looked as though he might have a stroke at any moment, his eyes bloodshot as he argued.

The manning agreements had been drawn up at national level, but the firm's chapel disagreed with them, and were insisting on a separate agreement which would cost the Gazette a great deal of money.

Pete Turner seemed adamant, yet Leigh could see that the Imperial Chapel were not fully backing him, since the members of other unions stood to lose a great deal if the strike continued.

At midnight, Matt made a firm compromise offer, which Pete Turner angrily rejected. At one o'clock Matt made it again, slightly improved, and this time the union negotiating committee said that they would like to discuss it in private.

Matt stood up. 'You stay here,' he said. 'We'll leave you for half an hour. I imagine we could all do with a break.'

The other executives dashed off to phone their wives and make apologies for absence, while Matt wandered into his own office and sat down on his chair, his head dropping into his hands. Leigh looked at him silently, aching with love. He looked worn out.

She moved behind him and gently began to massage the taut neck muscles, her fingers smoothing his skin. He groaned. 'Oh, that's terrific!'

She looked at his bent dark head, tracing the silver hairs she could glimpse among the black. How much more of this sort of burden could he take?

'I thought you'd gone,' he said abruptly, his voice smothered in his hands.

Leigh massaged silently, feeling the deep tension of the muscles seeping gradually away beneath her fingers.

A man appeared in the doorway, and Leigh felt a quiver of alarm as she recognised Joe Lord, Cathy's father, a broad, distinguished man of fifty-five, his eyes coldly intent as he took in the intimacy between herself and Matt.

Leigh's hands halted. Matt looked up. There was a slight, tense silence.

'How's it going, Matt?' Joe Lord asked, his voice brusque.

'Bloody difficult,' Matt said tersely.

'Any chance of a settlement tonight?'

'God knows.'

Joe Lord grimaced. 'It will cost us a fortune. We can't afford a stoppage.'

Matt straightened his weary shoulders. 'No,' he said, his voice flat.

Leigh could feel the tension flowing back into him again, and her fingers moved to his neck, tenderly stroking the cramped muscles beneath the black hair. He suddenly leaned backward so that his head lay against her breasts. Leigh felt her heart stop. Her blue eyes moved to Joe Lord's face.

He was looking stiffly at them, his eyes unreadable. Coughing slightly, he said, 'Well, if you need advice, I'm at home, Matt. You can call me any time.'

Matt nodded. 'Thank you, Joe.' His tone was polite but made it clear that he was unlikely to ask for Joe Lord's help. The older man nodded and left, closing the door behind him. Matt closed his eyes, his head wearily resting on Leigh. She tenderly let her fingers stray through the black hair, soothing him silently. A long sigh came from him and his body sagged.

'Would you like some tea?' she asked softly. 'Or whisky?'

He shook his head. 'Just keep doing that,' he said. 'It's very soothing.'

She smiled to herself, continuing to stroke his hair. The silence deepened until she began to think he had fallen asleep. He leaned so heavily against her, his lean body relaxed, his eyes closed, all the weary lines of his face smoothed out.

Suddenly the telephone began to shrill. She leaned over and picked it up, listened, answered and put it down. Matt straightened, the fighting look back in his grim eyes and mouth.

'They want to start again,' she said.

Matt nodded. 'I'm going to the cloakroom. I'll wash my face, comb my hair and be there in five minutes. See if you can rustle up some more food and drink, Leigh. I think we're all going to need the blood sugar.'

She obeyed, relieved to be busy, and went into the board room. The men were looking grey and tired, too. Leigh went to the windows and opened them, then began deftly to clear the littered table of all but the essential things they needed. They watched her as she moved between them, that curiosity in their eyes. She was aware that every one of them believed her to be Matt's mistress, but not a hint of it showed on their weary faces.

When Matt walked into the room a moment after she had finished, the room smelt clearer and cleaner, the chill night air was blowing away the stale scents and the men were tidying the piles of their papers, sitting forward in their chairs, that first depressing gloom gone.

Matt sat down in his chair, his lean body erect. He had washed in cold water, she suspected, by the glow in his pale face. His hair was combed neatly. His tie was back. The toughness seemed to be restored to his facial muscles, that weary droop gone.

The food arrived, and she helped to distribute it. The men ate ravenously, relaxed around the table. For the moment the discussions were in abeyance. They all felt the need of a break. Some of the union negotiators vanished briefly, returned looking slightly better. Pete Turner had also washed in cold water, she guessed, from his pale face. His forehead no longer glistened with perspiration, but the lines of weariness were cut as deeply into his face as into Matt's.

After this pause, the talks began again. Leigh sat at Matt's shoulder, just out of his line of vision, listening. As the hours passed his throat was dry, his voice strained.

Once while Pete Turner was talking Matt glanced down sideways at the slender grace of Leigh's long silk-clad legs, and then up at her profile. Although she did not meet his eyes her heart quickened. He turned back towards Pete again and the brief flash of awareness faded.

Daylight had begun to seep into the room when the deadlock was finally resolved. Matt had somehow talked the men into a compromise, although both sides had had to give away something they were reluctant to concede. They had lost some money, she thought, but at least the strike was over. By sheer ruthless persistence, Matt had talked his way through it.

Slowly the men began to drift away. Matt stowed sheafs of papers into his case. Pete Turner yawned, stretching, and met Leigh's calm eyes.

'Tired?' he asked her, quite gently.

'Exhausted,' she agreed, smiling at him. 'But not as tired as you are, Mr Turner, I don't imagine.'

He grinned. 'Well, we got something, and something is always better than nothing.'

Matt looked at him in an odd, hard way. 'Yes,' he said levelly, 'something is better than nothing.'

Pete said goodnight and left. The room was empty, the smoke-filled air, the littered table, the only signs of the recent trouble.

'I'll drive you home,' said Matt.

'I'll get a taxi,' Leigh murmured.

'Don't argue, Leigh, for God's sake,' he said, his face set in grey lines.

She said nothing more, following him into the lift and out into the car park. As they drove out of it she saw a car full of their recent companions inching out of a bay. Eyes followed them. What did it matter what anyone thought? she told herself. All that mattered was Matt, and the dead, worn look on his face hurt her deeply.

He pulled up outside Sam's house and she got out. She was taken aback when he did so, too, facing her across the top of the car, his hand pushing back a lock of silvered hair which the cold autumn wind blew across his temples.

She looked at him anxiously. 'Matt, you're dead tired. Go home to bed.'

'This won't wait,' he said, his grim mouth issuing the words wearily, as though it took all his energy to say them.

She was too concerned to argue. Sighing, she led the way into the house and up the stairs. He followed her into her flat, halting as he saw her cases standing in the centre of the room. Leigh flushed, seeing his eyes on them.

He turned and looked at her, his hands driven into his pockets. 'You were going,' he said in that weary voice.

She didn't answer, looking at him. After a pause, she said, 'I could make you some tea. Would you like some?'

Matt nodded without replying, and she moved into the kitchen. After putting on the kettle, she asked, 'Anything to eat?'

He came into the kitchen slowly. She could see by the way he moved that he was bone tired, so exhausted he could only just stand.

'Shut your eyes,' he ordered.

She frowned. 'What?'

'Shut your eyes.' The pale mouth formed the syllables stiffly.

Leigh obeyed. Was he going to kiss her? She knew she was beyond denying him anything he wanted.

Instead he took her hand. She felt his fingers move against hers, then the cold touch of metal. Her eyes opened in astonishment. On her left hand the blaze of the square cut sapphire ringed with diamonds was dazzling. She looked at him in silent disbelief.

Matt watched her with those grim, weary grey eyes, saying nothing. His face was unreadable.

She swallowed, her lips dry. 'Are you asking me to marry you, Matt?' It was so unexpected, so unbelievable, that she was curiously cold.

'You've belonged to me since the first day we met,' he said in a dry voice. 'I told you I'd stamp Hume all over you. This just makes it official.'

Her eyes tried to penetrate the tired mask. 'And Cathy Lord?'

He shrugged the question away. 'There was no way I would have married a child of her age. For God's sake, Leigh, I've known her since she was a baby. I'm fond of her, but she's no wife for a man of my age. She's still an adolescent.'

The kettle began to boil and she moved to make the tea. 'Would you like some toast with it?' she asked him.

He yawned. 'God! I'm so tired I can only just keep my eyes open. The tea will do.' He staggered back into the sitting-room and she heard him collapse on to the couch. Quickly she poured him a cup of tea and went back to him. He was already asleep, slumped against the back of the couch, his face shadowed.

Leigh stood looking at him, her own weariness forgotten. He looked almost old. She hated time for stealing from her as it carved those lines upon his hard face. Gently she knelt to take off his shoes, then swung him on to the couch full length. He muttered drowsily as she raised his head to slide a cushion beneath it. Covering him with several blankets, she put out the lamps and went to bed herself.

She had no time to speculate about his motives in marrying her. Sleep fell upon her like a wolf before her eyes had done more than close. She slept deeply, woken at eight by the sound of her own doorbell. Hurriedly slipping into a silk wrap, she rushed to the door. Matt struggled out of his blankets, his hair tousled, his unshaven face grim.

Sam stood at the door, a curious hard look on his face. His eyes slid over Leigh with a flicker of embarrassment. 'Good morning, miss,' he said, oddly formal.

'I shan't be needing a lift to work this morning, Sam,' she said calmly.

Matt appeared behind her shoulder, running a hand through his ruffled black hair, yawning violently.

Sam looked at him stubbornly. 'I saw your car outside, Mr Hume,' he said.

A mocking look came into Matt's eyes. 'Why the cold front, Sam?' he asked drily.

Quickly, seeing the disapproval in Sam's eyes, Leigh held out her left hand. 'Do you like my ring, Sam?'

Sam's face changed and a smile came into his eyes. She saw the concern and disapproval fade. He looked at Matt. 'It's very nice indeed,' he said. 'Congratulations, Matt.'

Matt grinned at him, insolence in the tilt of his head. 'Thank you, Sam,' he said. 'I trust you'll spread the news for us. It's time the Gazette grapevine revised its version of the situation.'

Sam looked stolidly at him. 'Yes, indeed, Matt,' he said.

When he had gone, Leigh looked at Matt, a wry expression on her face. 'You shouldn't have teased him. I like Sam.'

'So do I,' he said, turning away. 'What's for breakfast? I'm starving.'

'You've only had a few hours' sleep,' she said in concern. 'It was five when we got back here. Go back to bed for a while, Matt.'

'Come with me,' he said.

Her face coloured deeply. She made no answer. He

looked round at her, his eyes speculative.

'You would if I meant it, wouldn't you, Leigh?'

'Yes,' she said, meeting the irony of his glance without evasion.

He took her chin in his hands, staring into her blue eyes. 'When will you marry me?'

'When you like,' she said.

His mouth twisted. 'So submissive, Leigh. Will you always be this sweet?'

She made no answer, looking back at him calmly.

'You haven't even asked me any questions,' he said slowly. 'Are you going to?'

'No,' she said.

'Why not?' His eyes were unreadable.

'I'm taking each day as it comes,' she said frankly.

'Your new scheme for living, Leigh?' His voice was wry.

'Yes,' she said. He wanted her, that was all she needed to know. She no longer cared about anything else.

He hesitated, as though on the point of saying something, then shrugged. 'Maybe you're right. What about that breakfast?'

Leigh moved into the kitchen and began to prepare him a meal. In the last twenty-four hours her whole life had seemed to turn upside down. The pains, the frets, the puzzles of the time before had vanished. Now all she thought about was that Matt needed her, and whether his need was for a hot meal, a calming hand on his tired neck, or whatever he desired to take from her, she was prepared to give it to him without question: she had realised that when she saw him on the television the previous evening. The pleasures of giving whatever he demanded would be enough, she thought. What had Pete Turner said last night? Something is better than nothing.

CHAPTER TEN

THEY were married a month later. Leigh felt curiously
unreal as she drove away from the wedding reception
beside Matt, the smooth pale silk of her hair dressed to
perfection above the fur-trimmed, full-skirted blue coat
she was wearing. Autumn had faded into winter. The
bare trees fringing the road along which they drove made
twisting patterns upon the pale sky. A delicate sunshine
gave some colour to the day, but it was chilly, and across
the fields she saw hedges like dark scrambled wool and
the grey mist hovering in veils.

She had had no time to think much during the past
weeks. The news of their engagement had created an
enormous stir, both in the Gazette building and nation-
ally. There had been visits to be made to her own parents,
stunned and incredulous as they made Matt welcome,
and to Matt's family in Hampshire. Leigh had felt incredibly nervous as he drove her down the long drive towards a flat façade and the cool elegance of a Georgian
house set in lawns and flowerbeds. Matt had given her a
little searching look as he parked, then taken her hand
firmly, his touch comforting.

His father was a much older version of himself, his
store of energy fading, courteous, shrewd, watchful. His
mother had proved to be an elegant, thin-faced woman in
her sixties, very well preserved and cool in her manner.
Leigh had sensed that neither of them was exactly delighted with the engagement, but Matt's possessive

manner had made it plain to them that, whatever their feelings, all was settled.

It had been a relief to leave, although neither of them had been unpleasant. The restrained atmosphere had been stiff with unspoken doubt.

Leigh's parents had been warmer, protesting a little at the speed of Matt's plans, but falling in with them when he made it clear he was not prepared to wait. The wedding had been from her own home, of course, and her mother had been worn out with all the plans by the time the wedding day arrived. Leigh's decision to continue working for Matt had met with disbelief from her parents, but Matt had backed her decision firmly. She had half expected him to argue about it at the time, but to her relief he had merely nodded. She wanted to be with him all day, the idea of leaving him to another woman's protection during his long working hours intolerable.

They had been kept hard at work throughout the period. The running fight between unions and management went on daily. Leigh had almost forgotten her approaching wedding at times, so deeply did the job engross her, and although she saw a good deal of Matt outside the office there had been no intimacy in their meetings. He took her out to dinner, came back to her flat, listened to music and relaxed, the dominating passion of his love-making totally absent from their relationship.

While they were on their honeymoon his deputy would take over running the firm. Leigh made sure that the man's secretary knew all she needed to know, then on the Friday she and Matt drove up to Leicester together.

Matt stayed at a local hotel for the night. Leigh spent the evening quietly, her nerves jumping as she accepted the reality of what was to happen next day. Cathy Lord had gone to America during the past weeks and Leigh and Matt had never discussed her. But she had wondered, painfully, what Ann made of the news, and was surprised and pleased to get a present and card from her, the brief message making it plain that Ann had, as Leigh had predicted, got over her infatuation. That Ann was astonished by the turn of events was clear, but Leigh was glad to realise that her marriage would not hurt her cousin.

Matt had inspected their wedding presents at the reception, a lift of his brow towards her indicating that he had noticed the silver rose bowl which she had received from Phil. Her colour rose. She was glad he had not seen the note Phil included with it. Phil had not yet got over her, she could sense, and there was jealous irony in his congratulations.

When she had come down the aisle towards him, her slender body graceful in the delicate silk and lace of her gown, winter sunlight had glinted on the blonde hair beneath her full veil, revealing to her Matt's hard face as he glanced round at her. She had been cold and shivering. His fingers had tightened on hers as he took her hand, and beneath the formal music of her vows she was aware of surrendering herself to him completely, her oval face grave at the implications of her act. From that moment onwards, she had thought, however he hurt her, she belonged to him. Glancing at him beneath her lashes she had wondered what he was thinking, leanly elegant in morning suit, his grey eyes unreadable.

Matt had asked her to choose a honeymoon spot, and she had decided not to go abroad, since the pressure of work demanded that they limit their honeymoon to one week only. Her parents had protested at her decision, but Matt had overruled them, showing preference for a week spent in a house in the depths of quiet Cambridgeshire. His cousin Alastair owned the place, he told her, and was abroad for a month in the Canaries. There was a pleasant caretaking couple who would look after them. They had a cottage in the grounds, so their presence would not disturb honeymoon privacy, he added drily.

'We can go abroad in the spring,' he added to her parents. 'Leigh would enjoy a trip to the Greek islands, I think. By then I shall be able to go with an easy conscience.'

As they drove towards Cambridgeshire now, Leigh glanced at him in faint uneasiness. Although they had spent most of the last month in each other's company hour after hour, they had been far removed from the ordinary engaged couple. Work bound them closer than passion. They shared a consuming interest in what they did, and they had grown more and more to depend upon each other in the small decisions of the day.

Remembering Matt's earlier assault upon her, she was puzzled by his present restraint. He had made no attempt to make love to her since he placed his ring upon her finger. He bewildered and worried her.

They arrived at the house and were welcomed by the caretakers, who, having shown them around, discreetly left them alone. They had left a delightful meal ready for them. Matt and Leigh ate in the lofty dining-room by the flickering light of candles, their manner strangely formal.

Afterwards, Matt pulled the decanter towards his plate and glanced at her warily. 'You go up to bed, Leigh. I'll have another glass before I come.'

Without a word of protest she obeyed. In their warm, pink-walled bedroom she undressed and got ready for bed like an automaton, not allowing herself to think. When she was ready she walked towards the bed, halting as a spasm of pain shot through her. She stood at the foot of the bed, her hand whitening as it clung to the heavy silk quilt.

Matt came into the room, taking in the tension of her body at a glance.

'What's wrong?' he asked abruptly.

'Nothing,' she said, her head turned away from him.

He moved, forcing her to look at him. His cold grey eyes marked the faint tears in her blue eyes.

'Don't lie to me,' he said tersely. 'Tell me.'

'Let me go, Matt,' she whispered. 'You're hurting me!'

He caught her by the shoulders, shaking her roughly. 'Tell me, Leigh!'

She felt a wild impulse to get away, struggling angrily. His hands lost control of her for a moment and she turned to run, but the ruthless fingers bit deep into her wrists, stopping her. She tugged vainly in an effort to escape, her slender body twisting in his grip. He stared at her, his eyes flickering over the white shoulders and arms, the gleam of her skin beneath the smooth cream silk of the nightdress.

'Cold feet, Leigh?' he asked between tight lips. 'I can soon change that.'

She fought desperately to stop him taking her into his arms, but she was no match for his sheer physical strength, and the hard mouth insistently searched across her face for her lips, the touch of it against her skin making her quiver. She turned her head aside with a sob to evade him and his mouth slid passionately down to kiss the warm, soft skin at the base of her throat, her pulse beating violently beneath his lips.

She pushed against his shoulders with both hands, breathing faster, and he abruptly tilted her head between his palms, her fine hair trickling over his fingers. She stared at the hard mouth as it moved nearer her own, and suddenly all the resistance drained out of her. She flung her arms around his neck, her hands dragging him nearer, and he laughed harshly. 'This is one battle I'll always win, isn't it, Leigh?'

She found his mouth without answering, kissing him wildly, sick with anguish as she did so, knowing that she did not want this physical mimicry of love. She wanted love itself. But if this was what Matt wanted, she would give it to him, however it hurt her.

When he pulled his head back his eyes moved over her restlessly, desire gleaming in the cold grey depths. 'I've waited for this moment for months,' he said unsteadily. 'Is the citadel mine, Leigh?'

'You know it is,' she said huskily. She shut her eyes and swayed against him, holding him with both hands around his neck. 'Take me, Matt. Don't torture me like this. Why have you waited so long? Are you determined to force me to my knees first?' She was shaking, her face buried in the brown strength of his neck. 'Don't make me say it, Matt, for God's sake!'

He was suddenly very still. A long hand twined in her hair, pulling her face away until he could look down into it. His skin was pale, his eyes very dark. 'What mustn't I make you say, Leigh?' he asked levelly.

'You know very well,' she muttered on a cry of misery. 'You warned me once that you would force my total surrender. You're a cruel, ruthless enemy, aren't you, Matt? Oh, God, why did I have to fall in love with you?'

The grey eyes stared deep into her tear-filled blue ones. A quiver of violent emotion ran over his hard face. 'Say that again,' he said jerkily.

A wild, miserable emotion was consuming her. She wanted to hit him, scream, behave in a way utterly alien to her nature. Anything which might relieve the pressing agony inside her would do. As if she were flinging weapons at him, she said bitterly, 'All right, Matt, have your victory ... what difference does it make? I'm crazy about you and you know it ... that's what you've been waiting to hear me admit, isn't it? All these weeks when you could have taken me without a struggle, you've been playing your waiting game just to hear me finally cave in and admit I love you.'

His arms came round her convulsively, pressing her head against his shoulder, his hand on the back of her head in a possessive gesture. She could feel his body trembling against her own, and his heart was racing wildly.

'How long have you been hiding it from me?' he asked shakily, his lips tangled in her hair. 'Oh, God, Leigh, I'd stopped hoping for it. Don't you know I've been insanely in love with you since the first day we met?'

Incredulity held her rigid in his arms. His hands were moving over her restlessly, and his voice whispered huskily into her ear. 'I took one look at you the day you walked into that hotel, and I felt as though fate had just kicked me in the teeth. I watched you, willing you to look at me, waiting for you to see me, because I was so sure you were mine. I couldn't conceive that the way I felt could be a one-way thing. Then those beautiful blue eyes looked right through me as though I were invisible, and I was stunned. I stared at you, seeing how the man with you was no more able to hold your attention than I was, and I thought ... my God, she's as cold as ice. I was burningly angry. I was so mad I wanted to knock that cool look off your face, but all the time underneath my rage I was thinking of nothing but getting you into my arms ...' His mouth slid down her hair and caressed her neck, a slow, warm sensuality in the movement.

Her heart was beating with a slow, heavy excitement. She had listened to every word with a growing sense of enchantment, hardly able to believe that it was Matt talking. From despair he had raised her to delight and pulsing relief. She put her hands on each side of his face, turning his head so that she could read the look in the grey eyes. The mockery, harshness, cruelty had gone. Flame leapt at her from the dark centres, and her breath caught.

'Matt,' she moaned, her eyes closing.

His mouth swooped hotly, and her hunger for him burst out of the bonds she had tried to place on it, her slender body shuddering as her response quickened.

He lifted her on to the bed, his arm reaching out to flick off the light, and she muttered protestingly as he moved away from her.

'Be patient, my darling,' he laughed softly, his voice very unsteady. A moment later she felt the silken slide of her nightdress as it was removed, and the cool male body rejoined her, arousing her to such a pitch that she was groaning with pleasure as he began to touch her. The damned-up hunger of months broke through the shattered walls between them, the sheer intensity of their desire sending flame over her skin.

Her dry lips parted against his throat, caressing the warm skin, a faint sob in her husky voice as she said, 'I love you, Matt, I love you . . .'

'Dearest,' he said hoarsely, his hands trembling as he slid them down her body, the warm palms lingering on her breasts. 'Keep telling me. I've waited so long to hear that note in your voice.'

His lips brushed tenderly between her breasts, his face turning to bury himself in the warm, soft whiteness beneath his cheek, and her fingers gently stroked the tight muscles of his neck, curling up into his black hair to wind themselves possessively among the thick strands.

The bodies moved erotically together, their mouths clinging. As Matt took her the wild clamour of her aroused senses deafened her to anything but the long-denied satisfaction of that deep, bittersweet, persistent, nagging ache. The piercing spiral rose like agony inside her, and Matt's breathing had a hoarse, anguished echo from her own.

They lay for moments afterwards, so close she heard his heart beating against her own, a silken relief covering them. Leigh was aware of sleep approaching softly, and, her slender body totally relaxed, made no effort to resist it. For the present her burning hunger had been extinguished, and she was incapable of thought. She had been so tired for weeks that now she let go of everything.

When she woke she was still in his arms, her face against his naked chest, hearing the heavy beating of his heart in her ear. Her eyes sleepily surveyed the grey morning light which was revealing the room. Matt's clothes lay in a scattered heap across the floor. She smiled, her eyes dancing, as she looked at them, and the faint movement of her mouth against his skin seemed to wake him.

He stretched lazily and the motion made her quiver with response. He glanced down, his dark lashes covering his eyes, and a teasing smile curved his mouth.

'At last I know the meaning of the phrase "master of all I survey",' he said insolently.

She bit him delicately. 'Brute!'

'Devil,' he whispered back, kissing her, feeling the pink mouth part in eager response. 'You made me wait for months, eating my heart out . . .'

She looked up at him. 'How was I to know you felt like that? You made sure I got no hint.'

'I didn't dare let you guess,' he said wryly. 'When I followed you up to your room, that first day, you froze me with a look of total indifference, and even when I'd discovered that I could get you to respond to me physically, I was bitterly aware that you were grimly determined to avoid any emotional entanglement.'

'I found you frightening,' she said, remembering her fear of him in the lift that day. 'I thought you were mad, stopping the lift like that, and then forcing me to accept your lovemaking. I was such a coward I couldn't bring myself to complain about the way you'd behaved, though. Oh, Matt, I have been such a coward. It was because I was afraid that I wouldn't even admit to myself that I was falling in love with you.'

He ran his fingers through the loose silken hair which fell over his shoulders. 'You have no idea how eagerly I watched for some sign that you were beginning to care for me. When you went out with Lianos I was almost insane with jealousy. I nearly let it all out that night. I was very tempted to stay and sleep with you, but I knew I'd never be able to hide how I felt if I actually got you into bed, so I forced myself to go. I had to stop you going out with other men, though, I couldn't bear the idea of another man touching you.'

'That was obvious,' she agreed, smiling teasingly. 'You puzzled me when you made me admit I wanted you so badly and then walked off without taking advantage of the situation. I was piqued and angry, I think. I couldn't make head nor tail of your behaviour.'

Matt grimaced. 'I thought I was pathetically obvious, Leigh. I waited for you to say something which would show you understood, but you never said a word.'

She looked at him cautiously. 'Matt, there's something I have to tell you . . .'

He caught the wary note in her voice and looked at her sharply. 'What?'

'You remember the typist in your office who was infatuated with you and had to be transferred?'

He frowned. 'Well?'

'She was my cousin,' Leigh said flatly. 'I'd heard all about you before I ever met you, and what I'd heard was not very attractive. I saw you as the man who had broken Ann's heart because of his cruel selfishness, and your behaviour in the lift that day merely seemed to underline the image I had of you.'

He groaned. 'Oh, God, so that's it!' He looked at her soberly. 'I didn't flirt with that child. I took her out to dinner and bought her chocolates and flowers because she'd worked hard that week. It seemed harmless enough. But she started to hang about, looking embarrassingly adoring, and in the end the gossip got out of hand, so I had no choice but to shift her out of the office.'

'Barbara told me that,' she said. 'And Ann seems to be over her crush on you now. She was always a soft-hearted girl.'

He frowned. 'I didn't see her at the wedding.'

Leigh smiled wryly. 'She didn't come. Too embarrassed, I expect.'

The grey eyes studied her oval features. 'I told you once we were the same kind of people. I didn't intend to hurt Ann. You didn't intend to hurt your fiancé. We both acted out of carelessness.'

Leigh looked at him soberly. 'That's true. It's a terrifying business, love, isn't it, Matt? I refused to have anything to do with it because it frightened me so much, only to discover I loved you just as I was planning to get as far away from you as I could.'

'The night Cathy scratched you?' His eyes questioned her. 'I could see it had affected you badly. Your face went white. After I'd got rid of her I went round to your flat and waited like a madman for you. I was desperate when you didn't show up and I had to go back to the Gazette to deal with that bloody strike. I sat there, trying to think clearly, when all I could think about was the possibility that you were already on a train to God knew where, and I might never find you again.'

'I very nearly went,' she said huskily.

'I knew that when I saw your cases afterwards,' he said, sighing. 'But when the board room door opened, and you came in, I felt the fear and tension drain out of me. I knew at that moment that I couldn't wait for you to fall in love with me. I had to marry you before I lost you for ever. I was past caring whether you returned my love or not. All I knew was that if I lost you I wouldn't feel alive any more.'

Leigh buried her face against him, kissing him adoringly. His hand stroked her hair, pressing her closer.

'I knew I loved you when I saw you on television in Sam's sitting-room, looking so desperately tired. Mrs Sam said you needed me, and my heart told me I needed you ... so I came.'

He held her close, both arms round her. 'Thank God you did,' he groaned.

She lifted her face and their mouths clung endlessly. He gave a rough sigh. 'I can't believe I've got you at last. The months since I first saw you have been unceasing torture. It was only made worse by knowing that I could get you into bed whenever I liked. The temptation that offered was hellish. I told myself that sooner or later I'd have your heart as well as your body, but after I knew you'd tried to run away I gave up hope of that. I decided to settle for what I could get. If your heart eluded me, I'd have your body, I thought, and you can't imagine how bitter that thought was.'

'I can,' she groaned. 'Tonight I was in hell at the same thought. Oh, Matt darling!'

He held her face between his hands, letting the silken cloud of hair trickle over his skin. 'How the hell I'm going to work with you in the office I've no idea, but when you suggested it I jumped at the idea because I wanted to have you around all the time. I thought you might learn to love me if you were with me all day, and I was so damned jealous I couldn't bear the notion that you might be at a loose end while I was away, and someone else might capture your attention.'

She looked amused. 'Were you afraid I'd be unfaithful to you, Matt?'

'Don't laugh, damn you,' he muttered, his voice slightly grim. 'When you showed me your ring that day in the lift I was so sick with jealousy I wanted to hit you. You were so cold and distant. I used every trick in the book to break you down.'

'And you soon did,' she said ruefully, remembering her own astonished inability to resist his lovemaking that day.

'I thought for a few hours that your response must mean I affected you the way you did me,' he said levelly. 'I soon realised I was wrong. I teased you to get a response from you. I could see that you would make short work of me if I tried to be serious. I had to annoy you, irritate you, bewilder you, to get your attention. And by hook or by crook I had to break your engagement.'

She caught a curious look in his eyes and frowned.

He made a wry face. 'There's one thing you still don't know, Leigh. I was in the lobby when I saw your fiancé with his party from the conference. I heard him say he was going up to your room, and I got up there fast, hoping things would work out just the way they did.'

She stared at him, dumbfounded. 'Then you did plan it?'

He grimaced. 'It was a despicable, underhanded trick, but I knew in every nerve of my body that you weren't in love with him, and I was frantic to get you away from him. So I walked in there and started making love to you, and you responded exactly as I'd hoped. He walked in at the perfect moment.'

She stared at him, speechless.

He gave her a rueful smile. 'Hit me if you like, and this time I won't hit back. When I left you that day I was crowing with triumph. I thought I'd ruined your engagement and left the field free for myself. That was why I sent you that letter inviting you for an interview.' He grinned. 'I was delirious with amusement as I imagined your face when you read it. I wanted you to come so badly, but I was afraid you might just tear it up. I would have found some other way of getting at you if you had, but the idea of making you my secretary was heady.'

'I couldn't resist coming,' she admitted. 'You annoyed me, but I was intrigued. You'd got under my skin.'

'I hoped desperately I had,' he said drily. 'What I hadn't bargained for was your honesty. When you told me you'd gone to his room I was terrified. For one moment I really thought he'd taken you, and you know, you cruel little cat, that that blow went right home.'

She looked at him yieldingly, her face soft. 'Yes,' she admitted, 'I suppose I knew that even then. You went quite white.'

'I felt sick,' he said harshly. 'For a while I could feel the physical after-effects of shock. You dealt me that blow deliberately and I saw your eyes register my pain.'

Her blue eyes were submissive under his look. 'Darling, I'm sorry. I didn't understand the instinct that made me try to hurt, but I wanted to see you wince.'

'Wince?' His mouth hardened. 'I nearly died of pain! That was the moment when I knew with certainty that I must never let you guess how I felt about you. If blind intuition had helped you to stab me like that, I shuddered to think what you would do to me if you ever found out I was helplessly in love with you.'

Leigh slid her palms up his bare chest, her fingertips

caressing. 'I swear I'll never hurt you again,' her voice promised softly. 'Matt, let me stay as your secretary. I want to be with you all the time, and I want to look after you. You work too hard. You need someone there to protect you.'

He looked at her through his dark lashes. 'You can stay, for the time being,' he promised. 'But only until the final phase of my private war against you is concluded.'

She was amused and puzzled, her blue eyes searching his hard, smiling face. 'You alarm me, Matt. What is the final phase of our war? I thought the war ended last night when you took both my citadels at once?'

His eyes teased. 'The first act of the conqueror is to storm the citadel,' he whispered. 'Afterwards, he makes certain it stays his property by leaving an army of occupation.'

She began to laugh, her blue eyes brilliant. 'An army, Matt?'

'Well, just one occupant to begin with,' he said wickedly. 'And until you're pregnant, darling, you can run my office as well as my home. Once we know you're going to have my baby, that's it. You'll have to choose your own replacement.'

Her eyes were taunting. 'Someone in her forties who's efficient and incorruptible and won't even look at you twice, Matt,' she said lightly.

His eyes burnt on her face. 'Could I make you jealous, Leigh? You were never jealous of Cathy, were you? I used to watch you to see the slightest hint of it, but you just looked at me coldly and so disapprovingly.'

'Cathy wasn't for you, Matt,' she said seriously, 'any more than I was for Phil. Even when I thought you meant to marry her, I knew you didn't love her.' Her lashes flickered on her cheek. 'But yes, you could make me jealous ... if I thought you showed any interest in a woman, in fact. I always knew you only felt amused affection for Cathy, and that didn't make me jealous. I was sorry for her.'

His face was grim. 'I was sorry for your fiancé, but my God! I was jealous of him, and of Lianos, and any man who so much as looked at you. That was why I moved fast to make sure the whole building knew you were mine. Do you think I didn't notice the way men looked at you everywhere we went? I wanted to surround you with a ten foot high wall.' A flickering wildness showed in the grey eyes. 'Tell me again that you love me. I want to hear you say it. I've waited to hear it for so many months.'

She kissed his shoulder, her blue eyes gently loving. 'I love you, Matt,' she said huskily. 'I came the night of the strike because I thought you needed me, and I married you for the same reason. I didn't believe you loved me, and it hurt like hell to become your wife thinking you would never feel the way I did, but when I took our wedding vows I was mentally handing myself over, lock, stock and barrel, for whatever you wanted, for the rest of my life.'

His eyes closed on a long sigh. He held her against him, his hand shaping and possessing the silken head. 'I accept the gift, Leigh, and I'll never let you go. You're mine at last, and it's for ever.'

She surrendered, relaxed against his hard body, cradled in total security in his arms, feeling the future flow like silk through her fingers.

What the press says about Harlequin Romances...

"...clean, wholesome fiction...always with an upbeat, happy ending."
— *San Francisco Chronicle*

"...a work of art."
— *The Globe & Mail*, Toronto

"Nothing quite like it has happened since *Gone With the Wind*..."
— *Los Angeles Times*

"...among the top ten..."
— *International Herald-Tribune*, Paris

Harlequin Presents...

The beauty of true romance...
The excitement of world travel...
The splendor of first love...

unique love stories for today's woman

Harlequin Presents...
novels of honest,
twentieth-century love,
with characters who
are interesting, vibrant
and alive.

The elegance of love...
The warmth of romance...
The lure of faraway places...

Six new novels, every
month — wherever
paperbacks are sold.

NEW FROM HARLEQUIN

YOUR 1980 ROMANCE HOROSCOPE!

Harlequin Reader Service

In U.S.A.
M.P.O. Box 707
Niagara Falls, NY 14302

In Canada
649 Ontario Street
Stratford, Ontario, N5A 6W2

Please send me the following Harlequin Romance Horoscope volumes. I am enclosing a check or money order of $1.75 for each volume ordered, plus 40¢ to cover postage and handling.

☐ **Aries**
(Mar. 21-Apr. 20)

☐ **Taurus**
(Apr. 21-May 22)

☐ **Gemini**
(May 23-June 21)

☐ **Cancer**
(June 22-July 22)

☐ **Leo**
(July 23-Aug. 22)

☐ **Virgo**
(Aug. 23-Sept. 22)

☐ **Libra**
(Sept. 23-Oct. 22)

☐ **Scorpio**
(Oct. 23-Nov. 21)

☐ **Sagittarius**
(Nov. 22-Dec 22)

☐ **Capricorn**
(Dec. 23-Jan. 20)

☐ **Aquarius**
(Jan. 21-Feb. 19)

☐ **Pisces**
(Feb. 20-Mar 20)

Number of volumes checked @ $1.75 each $_____

N.Y. and N.J. residents add appropriate sales tax $_____

Postage and handling $____.40

TOTAL: $_____

I am enclosing a grand total of $_____

NAME_____

ADDRESS_____

STATE/PROV._____ ZIP/POSTAL CODE_____

PRS 328